Homemade

STRAWBERRY JAM

"It's all in knowing how"

HOMEMADE JAM
Strawberry
July '56

HOMEMADE JAM
Strawberry
July '56

Home Baking Made Easy
FOR BEGINNERS AND EXPERTS

RETRO BAKING RECIPES

Delicious teatime treats illustrated with retro-style artwork by Martin Wiscombe

SALMON

Index

Printed and Published by Dorrigo, Manchester, England. © Copyright.
All rights reserved. No part of this publication may be reproduced, stored in a retrieval system or transmitted, in any form or by means, electronic, mechanical, photocopying or otherwise. Images Wiscombe Art/Recipes J Salmon Ltd

Chocolate Brownies

4 oz. good plain chocolate	1 teaspoon baking powder
4 oz. butter	5 oz. caster sugar
2 oz. flour	3 eggs, beaten

4 oz. chopped mixed nuts

Set oven to 350°F or Mark 4. Grease and line an 8 inch square baking tin. Melt the chocolate and butter together in a bowl set over, but not touching, a pan of simmering water. Sift the flour and baking powder into a mixing bowl, add the sugar, pour over the chocolate mixture and mix well together. Stir in the eggs and chopped nuts and mix well. Put into the tin, spread out and bake for 25 to 30 minutes until a skewer inserted comes out clean. Leave to cool in the tin for 10 minutes, cut into squares and turn out on to a wire rack.

Victoria Sponge Sandwich

6 oz. soft margarine	1 rounded teaspoon baking powder
6 oz. caster sugar	3 large eggs
6 oz. self-raising flour	4 tablespoons raspberry jam

Caster sugar for dusting

Set oven to 350°F or Mark 4. Grease and base line two 7 inch sandwich tins. Put all the ingredients, except the jam, into a bowl and beat well for 2 minutes until smooth and blended. Divide the mixture between the tins and bake for 25 minutes until golden brown and springy to the touch. Turn out on to a wire rack to cool. When cool, sandwich the cakes together with a generous layer of jam and dust the top with caster sugar. If desired, a layer of whipped cream can be added with the jam.

Shortbread

4 oz. butter   6 oz. flour
2 oz. caster sugar   2 oz. ground rice

Set oven to 350°F or Mark 4. Cream the butter and sugar together in a bowl. Gradually sift in the flour and the ground rice, kneading the mixture into a ball. On a floured surface roll or pat the dough into a round, ½ inch thick. Place on a plain baking sheet. Pinch up the edges and prick the top with a fork. Bake for about 35–40 minutes or until firm and pale golden. While still warm, cut into triangles and sprinkle with caster sugar.

Cherry Cake

8 oz. glacé cherries, halved	6 oz. caster sugar
3 oz. plain flour	Grated rind of 1 lemon
3 oz. self-raising flour	3 eggs, beaten
Pinch of salt	3 oz. ground almonds
6 oz. butter, softened	Milk to mix

Set oven to 350°F or Mark 4. Grease and line a 7 inch round cake tin. Rinse the cherries, dry well on kitchen paper and toss in a little of the flour. Sieve together the flours and salt twice to mix thoroughly. Cream together the butter, sugar and lemon rind in a bowl until light and fluffy. Add the beaten eggs a little at a time, beating well between each addition, keeping the mixture stiff and adding a little flour. Fold in the remaining flour, cherries and ground almonds with sufficient milk to make a fairly stiff dropping consistency; this will help to keep the cherries suspended evenly. Put into the tin and bake for 1 hour 20 minutes or until a skewer inserted comes out clean. Leave to cool in the tin for 5 minutes then turn out on to a wire rack.

Plain Oven Scones

8 oz. self-raising flour	¼ pint buttermilk, full cream milk
2 oz. butter	or soured milk
1 teaspoon caster sugar	Pinch of salt

Set oven to 450°F or Mark 8. Grease and flour a baking sheet. Sift the dry ingredients into a bowl and rub in the butter. Add sufficient of the milk to make a moist and spongy dough. Turn out on to a floured surface and knead gently. Roll out to ½ inch thickness and cut into rounds with a 2½ inch pastry cutter. Place on the baking sheet. Brush the tops with milk and bake for 8–10 minutes until risen and light golden in colour. Cool on a wire rack. Serve split in half with butter and jam.

For rich scones add 1 beaten egg to the dry ingredients before adding sufficient milk. Brush the tops of the scones with beaten egg rather than with milk.

Madeira Cake

4 oz. butter, softened	A few drops vanilla essence
5 oz. caster sugar	8 oz. self-raising flour
2 eggs	Milk to mix
¼ teaspoon salt	3 slices citron peel

Set oven to 350°F or Mark 4. Grease a 6 inch round cake tin. Cream together the butter and sugar in a bowl until light and fluffy. Beat in the eggs, salt and vanilla essence a little at a time with a little flour towards the end. Fold in the remaining flour a little at a time with sufficient milk to produce a soft consistency. Put into the tin and bake for 50 minutes. Remove from the oven, arrange the slices of peel in the centre and return immediately for another 10 minutes or until a skewer inserted comes out clean. Allow to cool in the tin for 5 minutes then transfer to a wire rack.

Butterscotch Biscuits

8 oz. light brown sugar	1 egg, beaten
4 oz. butter	12 oz. self-raising flour
1 teaspoon vanilla essence	½ teaspoon salt

Set oven to 350°F or Mark 4. Grease or line a baking sheet. Melt the sugar, butter and vanilla essence together in a saucepan very gently over a low heat. Remove from the heat. When the mixture has cooled add the beaten egg and mix together. Sift the flour and salt into a bowl. Make a well in the centre and pour in the cooled egg/fat/sugar mixture. Knead into a stiff dough. This will be fairly dry, but it needs no extra moisture. Roll out to ½ inch thickness on a floured surface and cut out the biscuits with a 2 inch cutter. Place on the baking sheet with sufficient space to allow them to spread. Bake for 20 minutes until light golden in colour. Allow to cool slightly before transferring to a wire rack. Makes 20–24 biscuits.

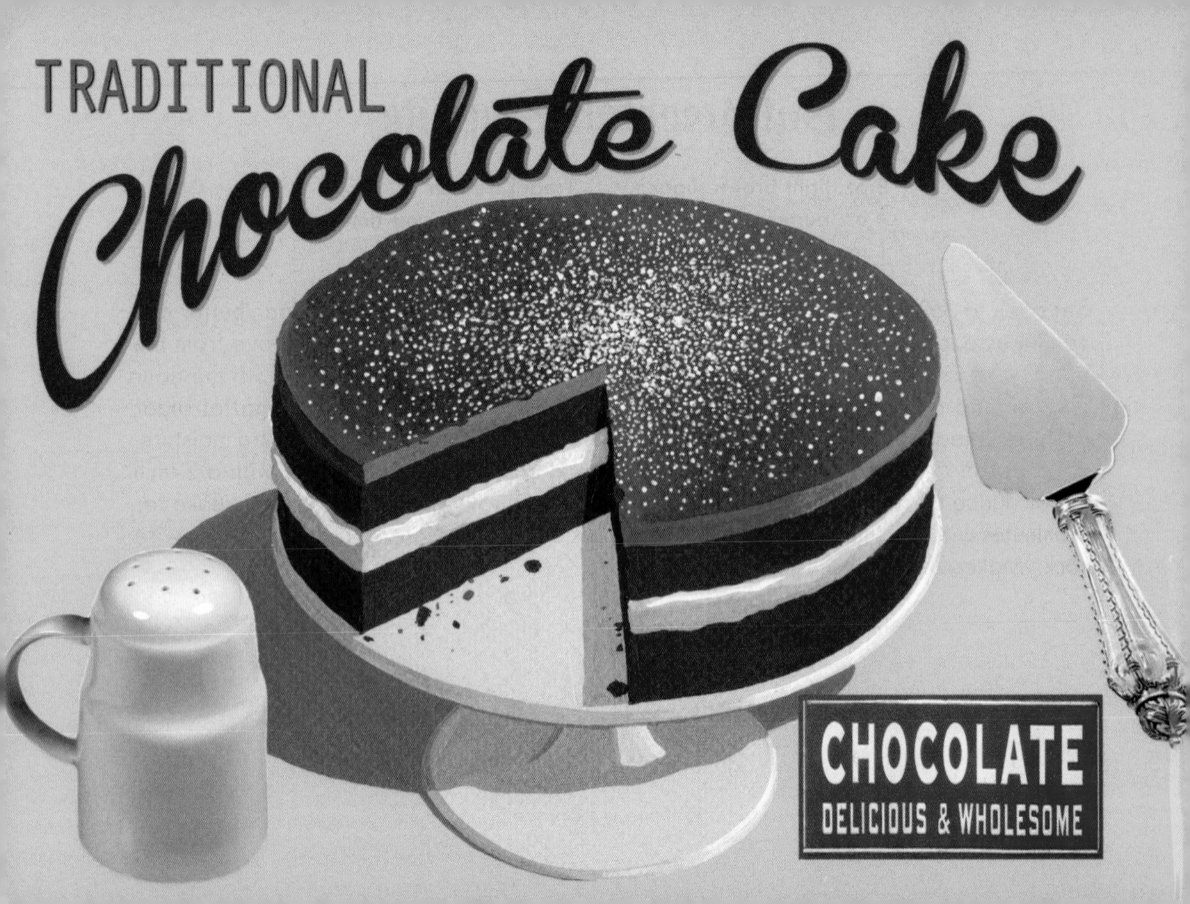
TRADITIONAL
Chocolate Cake
CHOCOLATE
DELICIOUS & WHOLESOME

Chocolate Fudge Cake

CAKE MIX

8 oz. flour   2 oz. cocoa powder   1½ teaspoons baking powder   3½ oz. butter
7 oz. caster sugar   3 eggs, separated   ¼ pint milk   Almond essence
Icing sugar, for sprinkling

FUDGE FILLING

1½ oz. butter   3 oz. plain drinking chocolate   1 lb. caster sugar
¼ pint cream or evaporated milk   4 teaspoons vanilla essence

Set oven to 350°F or Mark 4. Grease a shallow 8 inch x 12 inch baking tin. Sieve together into a bowl the flour, cocoa powder and baking powder. In another bowl beat the butter with a wooden spoon until it is creamy then beat in the sugar and the egg yolks. Stir in the mixed dry ingredients alternately with the milk, a little at a time. Finally, add a few drops of almond essence. Beat the egg whites stiffly and mix in as lightly as possible with a metal spoon. Put the mixture into the tin, spread out and bake for 50 minutes to 1 hour. Transfer to a wire rack to cool. Prepare the fudge filling by putting all the ingredients, except the essence, into a heavy saucepan over a low heat. Stir gently until melted then bring to the boil and continue until the mixture begins to thicken. Add the vanilla essence, beat until the mixture thickens then set aside until cool. When almost cold, spread over the cake and sprinkle with icing sugar.

Chocolate Madeleines

4 oz. flour	4 oz. butter
1 level teaspoon baking powder	2 eggs
1 oz. cocoa powder	Apricot jam
4 oz. sugar	Desiccated coconut

Glacé cherries and angelica, to decorate

Set oven to 400°F or Mark 6. Well butter 10 to 12 individual, deep dariole moulds. Sieve together into a bowl the flour, baking powder and cocoa powder. In another bowl beat together the butter and sugar until creamy, then beat in each egg separately and then stir in the dry ingredients. Three parts fill each tin with the mixture and bake for about 15 minutes or until the cakes feel firm. Turn out on a wire rack to cool. Warm a little apricot jam. When the cakes are cold, brush each top and side with jam, holding on a skewer to do so. Then roll in the coconut and decorate the tops with half a glacé cherry and pieces of angelica.

All-in-One Fruit Cake

6 oz. soft margarine	1 teaspoon ground mixed spice
6 oz. granulated sugar	10 oz. mixed dried fruit
2 eggs	2 oz. glacé cherries, halved
2 oz. self-raising flour	1 tablespoon milk
6 oz. plain flour	Pinch of salt

Grated zest of 1 orange (optional)

Set oven to 325°F or Mark 3. Grease and base line a 2 lb. loaf tin. Put all the ingredients into a bowl and mix until thoroughly blended. Put into the tin and bake for 1 to 1½ hours or until a skewer inserted comes out clean. Leave in the tin to cool.

Chocolate Macaroons

1½ oz. cocoa powder	4 oz. ground almonds
3½ tablespoons milk	Vanilla essence
White of 1 egg	Rice paper
8 oz. caster sugar	Blanched almonds, split, to decorate

Set oven to 350°F or Mark 4. First warm the milk and dissolve the cocoa powder in it thoroughly. Whip the egg white stiffly in a bowl, fold in the sugar and ground almonds and then the cocoa/milk mixture. Lastly add a few drops of vanilla essence. Place rice paper on a baking sheet and spoon on equal size heaps of the mixture, according to preference, leaving room for them to spread. Top each cake with a split almond. Bake for about 15 to 20 minutes until cooked and lightly browned and then transfer to a wire rack to cool.

Look at the colours!
Macaroons

Home Baking Made Easy
FOR BEGINNERS AND EXPERTS

It's all in knowing how

Cider Cake

4 oz. butter	1 teaspoon cinnamon
4 oz. caster sugar	8 oz. self-raising flour
2 medium eggs, beaten	½ pint cider

Set oven to 350°F or Mark 4. Grease and line a 7 inch round cake tin. In a bowl, cream the butter and sugar together until light and fluffy. Stir in the eggs, cinnamon and half of the flour. Gradually add the cider to this mixture and lastly add the remaining flour and mix thoroughly. Put into the tin and bake for about 45 minutes until firm to the touch, golden in colour and a skewer inserted comes out clean. Leave to cool and turn out on to a wire rack.

Date Slices

8 oz. stoned dates	4 oz. butter or margarine
¼ pint water	1 level teaspoon bicarbonate of soda
1 teaspoon vanilla essence	4 oz. quick cooking oats
4 oz. self-raising flour	6 oz. caster sugar

Set oven to 350°F or Mark 4. Grease a shallow 7 inch x 11 inch tin. Chop the dates and place in a saucepan with the water. Bring to the boil and cook until soft. Add the essence. Sift the flour into a bowl, rub in the fat, add the bicarbonate of soda and stir in the oats and sugar. Put half the crumbly mixture in the tin and press down firmly. Cover with the dates, top with the rest of the mixture and press down. Bake for 20–30 minutes. Leave to cool in the tin and when cool, dredge with icing sugar and cut into slices.

Carrot Cake

8 oz. soft brown sugar   2 fl. oz. water   8 oz. carrots, peeled and grated
4 oz. raisins or currants   8 oz. flour   3 oz. butter   4 oz. chopped nuts
1 level teaspoon salt   1 level teaspoon bicarbonate of soda
2 level teaspoons baking powder   ½ level teaspoon mixed spice
2 level teaspoons ground cinnamon

Set oven to 325°F or Mark 3. Well grease a deep 7 inch square cake tin. Put the water, sugar, raisins, carrots, spices and butter in a saucepan over a low heat until the sugar has dissolved, stirring all the time. Then boil for 3 minutes. Remove from the heat and leave until the mixture is tepid. Then stir in the sieved flour, salt, baking powder, bicarbonate of soda and nuts. Mix well together. Place in the tin and bake for about 1 hour until firm and a skewer inserted into the cake comes out clean. Leave in the tin for 15 minutes to cool and then turn out on to a wire rack. Keep for 24 hours before serving sliced and buttered. This cake keeps well.

Picnic Slices

8 oz. plain or milk cooking chocolate

2 oz. butter

4 oz. caster sugar

2 oz. glacé cherries, chopped

1 egg, beaten

4 oz. dessicated coconut

2 oz. sultanas

Set oven to 300°F or Mark 2. Grease a Swiss Roll tin. Break the chocolate into pieces and place in bowl over hot water. When the chocolate is melted, pour into the bottom of the Swiss Roll tin and leave to set. Meanwhile, cream the butter and sugar together in a bowl and add the beaten egg, coconut, sultanas and chopped cherries. Mix well and spread evenly over the chocolate base. Bake for 30 minutes until golden brown. Leave to cool slightly in the tin then cut into slices with a sharp knife and transfer to a wire rack.

Date and Walnut Cake

CAKE MIX

8 oz. stoned dates, chopped   1 breakfast cup boiling water
1 teaspoon bicarbonate of soda   3 oz. butter   8 oz. sugar   1 large egg, beaten
1 teaspoon vanilla essence   10 oz. flour   1 teaspoon baking powder   ½ teaspoon salt

ICING

2½ tablespoons demerara sugar   1 tablespoon butter   1 tablespoon single cream

Set oven to 350°F or Mark 4. Grease and line a 12 inch x 9 inch tin. Pour the boiling water over the chopped dates and add the bicarbonate of soda. Let this stand. Meanwhile cream the butter and sugar together in a bowl. Add the beaten egg and stir in the vanilla essence. Add the flour, baking powder and salt. Add the date mixture to the cake mixture and mix well. Pour this runny mixture into the tine and bake for 40 minutes. When cool cover with icing and when set turn out or cut into slices.

Icing: Mix together the demerara sugar, butter and cream in a saucepan. Bring to the boil and boil for 3 minutes, stirring constantly. Cool a little and pour over the cake. Scatter with chopped walnuts.

Lemon Cake

4 oz. soft margarine   6 oz. caster sugar   2 large eggs   6 oz. self-raising flour
Grated rind of 1 lemon   4 tablespoons milk

SYRUP
3 rounded tablespoons icing sugar   3 tablespoons fresh lemon juice

Set oven to 350°F or Mark 4. Grease and bottom line a 2 lb loaf tin. Cream the margarine and sugar together in a bowl until light and fluffy. Add the eggs, flour, finely grated lemon rind and milk. Mix well to a soft, dropping consistency. Put into the tin, smooth the top and bake for 40 to 45 minutes until firm and a skewer inserted comes out clean. For the syrup, mix the sifted icing sugar and lemon juice together in a bowl and pour over the cake as soon as it comes out of the oven. Leave in the tin until completely cold.

Tea and Cakes

Cup of Tea 6d
Pot of Tea 9d
Cakes .... from 6d

Apple Scones

8 oz. wholemeal self-raising flour   1 teaspoon ground cinnamon
1 teaspoon baking powder   4 oz. butter   2 oz. soft brown sugar
2 medium sized cooking apples, peeled, cored and finely diced
1 medium egg

Set oven to 375°F or Mark 5. Mix the dry ingredients together in a large bowl. Rub in the butter, stir in the sugar and the diced apple and lastly stir in the egg. Mould the mixture into 10 or 12 heaps (as you would for rock buns) and place on a floured baking tray. Bake for 20–25 minutes. Cool slightly before transferring to a wire rack. Serve split, with butter.

Banana Cake

9 oz. self-raising flour
10 oz. sugar
4 oz. margarine, softened
3-4 ripe bananas, mashed
2 eggs

½ teaspoon salt
1 teaspoon vanilla essence
½ teaspoon bicarbonate of soda
Jam, to choice
Whipped cream

Set oven to 375°F or Mark 5. Grease and line two 9 inch sandwich tins. This cake is best made in a food mixer. Put all the ingredients, except the bananas, together into the mixer bowl and mix on medium speed. When blended stir in the well-mashed bananas. Turn into the two tins and bake for 25–30 minutes. Turn out on to a wire rack to cool. When cool sandwich together with jam and whipped cream. Alternatively this cake can be served plain.

This cupcake is mine

How TO GET THE MOST OUT OF YOUR *Sunbeam* MIXMASTER

Fruit Buns

12 oz. flour	3 oz. sugar
4 oz. ground rice	3 oz. currants
2 teaspoons baking powder	2 eggs, beaten
4 oz. butter	Milk

Set oven to 400°F or Mark 6. Mix the flour, ground rice and baking powder together in a bowl. Rub in the butter until the mixture resembles fine breadcrumbs, then stir in the sugar and currants. Mix in the eggs and sufficient milk to make a smooth firm paste. Turn out on to a lightly floured surface and roll out to 1 inch in thickness. Cut into 2 inch rounds and place on a greased baking sheet. Bake for 15 to 20 minutes until golden.

Seed Cake

6 oz. butter, softened   1 heaped teaspoon caraway seeds
6 oz. sugar   8 oz. self-raising flour
3 eggs, separated   3–4 drops of almond essence
Milk to mix

Set oven to 350°F or Mark 4. Grease and line a 7 inch round cake tin. Cream together the butter and sugar in a bowl until light and fluffy. Whisk the egg whites in a bowl and then beat in the yolks. Combine gradually with the butter and sugar mix. Sprinkle in the caraway seeds and fold in the flour, adding the almond essence. If necessary, add sufficient milk to the mixture to make a thick batter. Put into the tin and sprinkle a few caraway seeds over the top of the cake. Bake for 1 hour or until a skewer inserted comes out clean. Leave to cool in the tin for 5 minutes then turn out on to a wire rack.

Flapjacks

8 oz. rolled oats   3 oz. caster sugar
4 oz. butter or margarine   2 tablespoons golden syrup

Set oven to 350°F or Mark 4. Grease an 11 inch x 7 inch baking tin. Gently heat the butter or margarine, sugar and golden syrup together in a pan until all are melted. Gradually stir in the rolled oats, combining well with the syrup mixture. Press into the tin and cook for about 20 minutes. Mark into fingers and leave in the tin to cool. When cold turn out and break up; the flapjacks should still be soft and moist.

Coffee Cake

CAKE MIX

6 oz. soft margarine   6 oz. sugar   2 heaped teaspoons instant coffee granules
1 tablespoon hot water   3 eggs, beaten   7 oz. self-raising flour
Pinch of salt   1 teaspoon baking powder

ICING and FILLING

4 oz. butter, softened   8 oz. icing sugar   1 tablespoon coffee essence
Chopped walnuts to decorate

Set oven to 375°F or Mark 5. Grease and base line two 8 inch sandwich tins. Cream the margarine and sugar together in a bowl until light and fluffy. Dissolve the coffee granules in the hot water. Beat in the eggs gradually, with a little flour with each addition. Sieve in the remaining flour with the salt and baking powder and fold in. Add the coffee mixture and mix well. Divide between the tins and bake for about 20 minutes until springy to the touch. Turn out on to a wire rack to cool. For the icing, mix the butter, sugar and coffee essence together in a bowl and blend well. Use to sandwich the cakes together and to cover the top. Finally, decorate with chopped walnuts.

Drop Scones

8 oz. self-raising flour   **½ teaspoon salt**   **1 level tablespoon caster sugar**
1 large egg   **½ pint milk**

Place the flour, salt and sugar into a bowl. Make a well in the centre and add the egg and the milk gradually, stirring to make a smooth, thick batter. Drop the mixture in tablespoons on to a hot, lightly greased griddle or heavy-based frying pan. Keep the griddle at a steady, moderate heat and after 2–3 minutes when bubbles show on the surface of the scones, turn over and cook for 2 more minutes. Place the finished scones in a warm, folded tea towel; this will keep them warm and by keeping in the steam will prevent them from drying out. Serve warm with butter and jam or honey.

Boiled Fruit Cake

4 oz. margarine	9 oz. self-raising flour
4 oz. soft brown sugar	1 egg, beaten
8 oz. mixed dried fruit	½ teaspoon salt
¼ pint water	1 level teaspoon mixed spice

Put the margarine, sugar, dried fruit and water into a saucepan, bring slowly to the boil and simmer for 5 minutes. Allow to cool. Set oven to 325°F or Mark 3. Grease and line a 7 inch cake tin. Put all the remaining ingredients into a bowl, add the cooled fruit mixture and mix to a thick batter. Place in the tin and bake for 1½ hours or until a skewer inserted into the cake comes out clean. Leave to cool in the tin for 10–15 minutes and turn out on to a wire rack.

TEA

Please

Village Fete
TEA TENT

Cup of Tea	6d
Pot of Tea	9d
Cakes	from 6d
Lemonade	5d
Orange Squash	3d

"One lump or two?"

Chocolate Eclairs

¼ pint water	2 small eggs
1 oz. margarine	A few drops vanilla essence
Pinch of salt	Whipped cream
2½ oz. flour	Chocolate glacé icing

Set oven to 450°F or Mark 8. Grease baking trays. Put the water, margarine and salt into a saucepan and bring to the boil. Remove from the heat and add the sifted flour, beating well. Return to the heat and cook gently until the mixture leaves the sides of the pan clean. Remove from the heat, add the essence and beat in the eggs one at a time. Pipe the mixture on to the baking trays, using a plain vegetable pipe (the size of the eclairs depends on personal preference). Bake for 25–30 minutes. When cold, split and fill with whipped cream and coat with chocolate glacé icing.

Rich Plum Cake

8 oz. butter	4 oz. glacé cherries, halved
8 oz. caster sugar	8 oz. flour
6 medium eggs, lightly beaten	8 oz. chopped mixed peel
8 oz. currants	8 oz. almonds, blanched and chopped
8 oz. raisins	2 tablespoons rum or brandy
8 oz. sultanas	1 tablespoon black coffee

Set oven to 325°F or Mark 3. Grease a 9 inch round cake tin. In a bowl, cream together the butter and sugar until light and fluffy. Stir in the lightly beaten eggs one at a time with a teaspoon of flour after the third egg. Beat thoroughly. Mix all the dried fruit together with half the flour. Stir the rest of the flour, together with the peel and almonds, into the egg and butter mixture. Then add the floured fruit, the rum or brandy and the coffee. Put in the tin and bake for 2½ hours or longer until a skewer inserted comes out clean. To prevent the sides from burning, tie a band of brown paper round the outside of the tin before baking. Leave to cool in the tin and turn out on to a wire rack.

Treacle Scones

12 oz. self-raising light wholemeal flour
3 oz. butter   1 dessertspoon black treacle
½ teaspoon salt   7 fl. oz. milk, approx.

Set oven to 400°F or Mark 6. Add the salt to the flour in a mixing bowl and rub in the butter until the mixture resembles breadcrumbs. Stir in the treacle and enough milk to make a soft dough. Roll out gently on a floured surface to about 1—1¼ inches in thickness and cut into rounds with a 2 inch pastry cutter. Place on a greased and floured baking tray and bake at the top of the oven for 10—15 minutes. Cool on a wire tray. Serve the scones cut in half and buttered; they are delicious with lemon cheese.

Honey Fruit Biscuits

1 level teaspoon clear honey
4 oz. butter
4 oz. soft brown sugar
1 large egg

1 oz. chocolate chips
Grated rind of 1 orange
2 oz. finely chopped nuts
Pinch of salt

8 oz. self-raising flour

Set oven to 350°F or Mark 4. Grease baking sheets. Cream the butter and sugar together in a mixing bowl until soft. Beat in the egg and honey and stir in the nuts, grated rind, chocolate chips and salt. Sieve in the flour and mix well. Divide the mixture into balls each the size of a walnut. Place about 2 inches apart on the baking sheets and flatten slightly with a floured fork. Bake for 10–15 minutes until pale brown. Leave to cool for a few minutes and then transfer to a wire rack. Makes about 36 biscuits.

Viennese Tartlets

8 oz. hard margarine	2 oz. cornflour
2 oz. icing sugar	1 teaspoon vanilla essence
4 oz. flour	Lemon cheese for filling

Set oven to 375°F or Mark 5. Put individual paper cases into about 18 patty tins. Cream together the fat and sugar in a bowl until really soft. Sift in the flour and cornflour and add the essence. Mix well. Place a little of the mixture in each paper case and hollow out the centre. Bake for 20 minutes. When cool dust with icing sugar and place a teaspoon of lemon cheese in each tart.

Farmhouse Gingerbread

10 oz. flour
2 level teaspoons ground ginger
2 level teaspoons ground cinnamon
1 level teaspoon bicarbonate of soda
4 oz. hard margarine

4 oz. soft brown sugar
6 oz. black treacle
6 oz. golden syrup
2 eggs, beaten
¼ pint boiling water

Set oven to 350°F or Mark 4. Grease and line an 8 inch square cake tin. Sift into a large bowl the flour, spices and bicarbonate of soda. Melt the margarine, sugar, syrup and treacle together in a saucepan over a slow heat, then pour this mixture into the dry ingredients. Mix well. Stir in the beaten eggs and lastly add the boiling water and stir. Pour this runny mixture into the tin and bake for 40–45 minutes until firm. Leave in the tin for about 10 minutes then turn out on to a wire rack. This cake improves in flavour if kept for 48 hours.

Lemon Tarts

BASE
3 oz. flour   2 oz. butter   ¾ oz. icing sugar   2 teaspoons cold water

FILLING
The juice of a small lemon   2 oz. caster sugar   1 egg   Icing sugar for dusting

Set oven to 375°F or Mark 5. Grease deep patty tins (makes approximately six tarts). Sift the flour into a bowl. Rub in the butter and add the icing sugar. Add sufficient of the water to make a moist dough. Roll out on a floured surface, cut into rounds and line the patty tins. Bake blind for 10 minutes. Remove from the oven and reduce temperature to 350°F or Mark 4. Meanwhile beat together the egg, caster sugar and lemon juice. Fill the pastry cases with the mixture and bake until set and the pastry is nicely browned. Serve hot or cold, but do not chill in the refrigerator.

Apple Cake

8 oz. self-raising flour   1 teaspoon salt   4 oz. butter, softened
4 oz. caster sugar   1 lb. cooking apples, peeled, cored and diced
1 medium egg, beaten   2 oz. currants
1 oz. chopped mixed peel   1 oz. demerara sugar for sprinkling

Set oven to 375° F or Mark 5. Well grease an 8 inch round cake tin. Sift the flour and salt into a bowl and rub in the butter until the mixture resembles breadcrumbs. Stir in the sugar, diced apple and egg and mix well. Add the currants and peel and stir in. Put into the tin, sprinkle the top with demerara sugar and bake for 30 to 40 minutes until golden and a skewer inserted comes out clean. Cool in the tin and turn out on to a wire rack. Serve, sliced spread with butter or, alternatively, serve warm with clotted cream as a pudding.

Pleasurings

Pleasuring Pamela

Nina Sheridan

LIBRIS

An *X Libris* Book

First published by X Libris in 1996

Copyright © Nina Sheridan 1996

The moral right of the author has been asserted.

A CIP catalogue record for this book
is available from the British Library.

ISBN 0 7515 1729 1

Photoset in North Wales by
Derek Doyle & Associates, Mold, Clwyd
Printed and bound in Great Britain by
Clays Ltd, St Ives plc

X Libris
A Division of
Little, Brown and Company (UK)
Brettenham House
Lancaster Place
London WC2E 7EN

For N.R.B.
– For whom with the Pleasure
There has to be love . . .

Chapter One

'*AND THIS WILL* be your room for the week, Mrs Lewis. I'll leave you to unpack now. Come down to the pool when you're ready – there's time for a swim before dinner.'

The girl, whose name badge called her 'Amanda', smiled a wide, professional smile and slipped out of the room quietly on her white, low-heeled pumps. Pam looked around her, still bemused by her lightning tour of the building. Elysium Hall was nothing like she had imagined a health farm should be.

This room for a start – decorated in soft peaches and green with cleverly placed, subdued lighting – looked more like a boudoir than a bedroom. It was certainly unlike any other hotel bedroom Pam had ever seen. The bed was wide and canopied in shiny, eau-de-Nil satin. Beneath the floral-patterned, opulently quilted cover, the sheets were pale apricot. Silk, she decided,

1

passing her fingertips across their surface.

Beneath her feet the cream carpet was thick and soft. The wardrobes were of pale, bleached wood, their glass panels lined with the same fabric as the bed canopy. A door leading off to the left led to a small but luxurious bathroom. The deep, extra-wide bath was the same delicate green as the canopy over the bed, the taps and fittings were all gold-plated, shining dully beneath the subtle ceiling spots which shed a diffused glow over the room.

There were towels, thick, fluffy, both peach and green, piled on a glass shelf to one side, and every toiletry Pam might ever want to use – bath oil, bubbles, talcum, body lotion – in complimentary sizes ranged across the self. In front of these, small phials of essential oils stood by a burner. All around the room there were candle holders with fresh, cream-coloured candles standing ready. There was even a lighter lying on the shelf. It seemed they had thought of everything.

What would Jeff think if he could see her now? Pam went back into the bedroom and stood before the full-length mirror in the corner of the room. Staring at her reflection, she could almost understand why her husband appeared to have lost interest in her. Her face was what she could only describe as ordinary: grey eyes, a straight nose which, she had always felt, ended slightly too soon, giving her a wide upper lip above a generous mouth. Her hair was fair rather than blonde, cut in a chin-length bob which always looked tousled, no matter how many times she brushed it, or how often she lathed it with mousse or hairspray.

She'd put on a little weight over the years, and could, if she was honest with herself, do with losing a few pounds. Otherwise she looked very similar now to how she had looked on her wedding day, barely five years before. Jeff had been interested in her then, pride shining in his light brown eyes as he smiled across the aisle at her.

Pam sighed as she thought of how, over the years, work had taken precedence over their relationship. Gradually, so slowly they had barely had a chance to notice it, they'd spent more and more time apart until suddenly, it seemed, they were strangers. Turning sadly away from her solemn-looking reflection, Pam set to unpacking her case. She jumped as the phone by the bed rang.

'Hello?'

'Pammie? You got there all right then?'

Pam felt a grin spread over her face as she recognised her older sister's voice on the line.

'Tiffany? Yes, yes I'm here. How's Paris?'

'Romantic, as usual. What do you think of Elysium Hall? Isn't it just *dee-vine*?'

'Well . . .'

'You relax now and let the staff take you over. Believe me, Pammie, one week at that place and you'll be a new woman!'

'Hmm. I'm not too sure if I want to be a "new woman", Tiff. What's wrong with the old one?'

'Nothing, idiot! Don't be so prickly! I just meant

3

that you're going to have a whale of a time. Mick and I always do! You need a break, love, especially after all that upset with Jeff. Relax and be pampered – you deserve it!'

Pamela grimaced at the telephone.

'You're right. I'm sorry if I sounded grumpy. I really appreciate your coughing up half the cost of this. I will enjoy it, I'm sure, once I get the feel of the place.'

'Sure you will. Call me when you get home, okay? I'll be back in London by the end of the week.'

'All right. Bye.'

Pam put the receiver back on its cradle as the connection was severed, feeling even more alone now than she had before. Damn it, this was no good! Tiffany had suggested she come here to relax and that was what she was going to do. To hell with Jeff and the fling he was having, to hell with her job and her boss with the wandering hands – this one week was for her and her alone and she was going to make the most of it!

The kidney-shaped swimming pool was deserted when Pamela arrived. She took the opportunity to study the three-part mural painted along one wall and was intrigued to realise that each section depicted the same naked woman in various erotic poses with a variety of different partners.

In the first, the woman's long, dark hair fell like a curtain across her face, concealing her expression as she knelt at the feet of an anonymous man. Her long, white hands gripped his thighs, her fingernails painted a bright, shocking scarlet, digging slightly into the taut flesh of his thighs. Though it wasn't explicit, it was obvious to Pamela that the woman was fellating the man, whose face was hidden by the spreading fronds of a curious-looking plant which had been painted as a division between that and the second mural.

Here, the same dark-haired woman was lying sprawled on a chaise placed in the centre of a rose garden. She was holding a pale yellow rose in one hand and a thorn had snagged the pale skin of her thumb. A bright bead of blood was welling on its tip. Just behind her, a naked man was bending to draw her thumb into his mouth.

Pamela felt a stirring between her thighs as she imagined the man's wet, warm tongue soothing the injured skin. Her soft sex-flesh began to pulse delicately as her eyes were drawn to the second woman who was kneeling on the grass, her face buried between the dark-haired woman's wide-flung legs.

Drawing her eyes away uncomfortably, Pam focused on the third and final scene. This time the woman was bending over what looked like a table, her naked bottom, very white, held high. Her head and face could not be seen for she was bending away from the viewer. A girl was holding her arms, looking down at her with a loving expression as an ebony-skinned man, dressed in nothing but a leather mask, wielded a short cane over her upturned buttocks.

The stroke which was about to be administered was clearly not the first, for there was a single, red weal painted like a stripe across the woman's eagerly proffered behind. Pamela felt her secret flesh swell and moisten and was embarrassed by her arousal. This was not normally the sort of thing which turned her on.

Running her eyes from one end of the mural to the other, she was struck by the way in which one tiny part of each picture had been picked out in bright red. The woman's fingernails; the bead of blood on her thumb; the raised weal on her buttocks. As if the eye was meant to be drawn to these elements and to dwell on them.

Feeling hot and disturbed, Pamela turned her back on the mural and dived into the clear, sapphire blue of the water, shattering the calm surface. It was bliss to have a pool to herself and Pamela swam several lengths in her strong, confident crawl, trying to get the unwanted arousal out of her system. Back and forth she ploughed, cutting through the water until she was breathless. It was some minutes before she realised that she was no longer alone.

Perhaps she sensed someone else come in, but the realisation that she was being watched made her skin prickle warningly and she stopped virtually mid-stroke.

'Don't let me put you off.'

Pam looked up at the tall, loose-limbed stranger who was crouched at the end of the pool, watching her, and felt her breath catch in her chest. He was simply gorgeous – blond, tanned, with a square-cut jaw and broad shoulders shown to advantage in the blue singlet he was wearing. She could just see a generous growth of blond chest-hair beneath the neckline and her fingers itched to stroke it.

Her thoughts shocked her. That damn mural had a lot to answer for! She glanced up at him almost guiltily, as if afraid that he might have been able to divine her thoughts. He grinned at her before consulting the clipboard in his hand.

'It's Pamela, isn't it?'

Pam nodded, irrationally irritated that he clearly knew she was attracted to him. She had always disliked that kind of confidence in men, especially men more handsome than they ought to be, like this arrogant specimen.

'I'm Luke,' he told her.

Pam had to bite her tongue. What she wanted to say was *well, you would be, wouldn't you?* She couldn't imagine for a minute that such a vision of masculine loveliness could ever be called John, or Bill.

'We recommend a session in the Jacuzzi when our clients first arrive – it's a good way to accelerate the winding-down process. Would you like to come through now?'

'All right.'

Pamela shrugged and waited for him to stand up before she hauled herself out of the water. To her surprise he didn't move, but just crouched there, watching her calmly. It was silly to expect him to turn away, she supposed, but she felt horribly self-conscious as she pulled herself up, out of the water. It ran down her body as she clambered inelegantly to her feet, her wet swimsuit moulding her generous curves with almost indecent closeness. She saw Luke's eyes flicker almost assessingly over her body.

Pam stared at him, too indignant to be embarrassed, and he smiled. For a moment she thought he was going to make some comment about her figure, or her ungraceful exit from the pool, but he merely stood and said, 'This way,' before walking ahead of her towards a door she hadn't noticed before on the far side of the room.

The Jacuzzi was small, suitable for only two or three people. On her own, Pamela had the chance to stretch her legs out in front of her and lean her head back against the padded side.

'Just relax, let your mind roam free,' Luke was saying as he pressed the button that would make the water bubble. 'You're quite alone here, you might like to take your costume off. I won't be far away – if you need anything, you only have to call.'

He smiled at her again as he left her alone, a slow, sexy smile which made Pamela's toes curl. She didn't want to be attracted to him, yet there was something about him, a kind of ... *knowingness* which, despite her initial wariness of him, made something tingle inside.

The lights grew dim as the warm, fragrant water began to hiss and bubble around her. Soft, restful music filled the air and Pam began to relax in spite of herself. Slipping the straps of her swimsuit off her shoulders, she sank down so that the gently pulsing jets of water could massage the back of her neck. She hadn't realised how tense she was until the fingers of warm spray began working on her bunched muscles.

Glancing around to check that she was indeed all alone, she wriggled out of her costume and put it on the side of the bath. Smiling to herself, she sank back down in the water and closed her eyes.

There was something deliciously decadent about lying naked in a jacuzzi. With her eyes closed Pam took Luke's advice and tried to empty her mind. The sounds of the gentle music and the softly bubbling water were soothing and she felt all the tension in her body slowly melt away. The lightly perfumed water caressed her skin, swirling across her breasts and along her inner thighs, breaking in tiny, rhythmical waves against the soft flesh of her vulva.

With a sigh, Pamela allowed her mind to turn to the images she had been blocking out for the past two weeks. She had not wanted to think of them before, they provoked too many strong and conflicting emotions which she found both uncomfortable and confusing. Now that she had the time and the space to analyse her feelings, she allowed herself to relive that awful night when she had gone unexpectedly to Jeff's office.

In her mind's eye, she opened the gate to the builder's yard and picked her way through the now silent machinery to the small unit from where Jeff ran his little empire. It was late – close to nine-thirty. Knowing he was working on a rush contract, Pamela had taken pity on him and bought a Chinese takeaway.

As she approached the office, she felt excited, looking forward to seeing his face when she arrived. They would share the meal, maybe even make love, as they had before, in the cramped space between the desk and the drawing board. The idea had made her pulses quicken – it had been so long since they had enjoyed each other like that. So long, come to think of it, since they had made love at all.

As she reached the steps leading up to the office, something had made her pause. Perhaps she had heard a sigh, or the creak of furniture, she couldn't decide, all she knew was that all was not as it should be.

Frowning, she crept up the last few steps and pushed the door open a crack. The sight which met her eyes made her breath catch in her throat and her body freeze.

Jeff was facing slightly away from her, so he did not notice her peering through the door. Not that he would have noticed anyway, for his entire concentration was taken up with what he was doing. His trousers were unfastened and had slipped slightly at the back to reveal the very tops of his buttocks. Dena, Pamela's so-called friend and Jeff's part-time secretary, was bent over the table, giving Pam a perfect view of her large, pink behind.

Jeff was gripping her hips, his fingers digging in to the soft flesh as he thrust in and out of her. Funny how the little details remain so clear in the memory, Pam reflected as she relived the scene. She remembered how Dena's skin had been slightly red where Jeff was holding her, as if his finger-marks would later turn into bruises.

Pamela had watched, wide-eyed, unable to move as her husband raced towards a climax. Dena was making little grunting noises, grinding her hips in a circular movement as he pulled out of her, rising up to meet him with each downward stroke. Pam had been transfixed by the sight of her red, wet labia as they sucked and pulled greedily at Jeff's cock and, to her horror and shame, she had felt her own sex-flesh moisten in response.

The hurt she felt at finding her husband *in flagrante* was tempered by her own blossoming arousal and she had watched, right up until the moment when Jeff let out a triumphant cry, pumping his hips back and forth into Dena's willing body before collapsing, breathless, across her back.

It was then that Pamela had crept quietly away, terrified that, now they had finished, they would turn round and find her watching.

Now, luxuriating in the warm, womb-like environment of the Jacuzzi, Pamela allowed herself to experience again those strange, illicit feelings of arousal. Hardly realising what she was doing, she opened and closed her legs, enjoying the play of water against her wakening sex.

11

She did not understand how the sight of her husband screwing another woman could have turned her on. The fact made her feel grubby and ashamed, and yet there was also a curiously piquant quality to that shame which added to her pleasure.

Now that she was alone and so far removed from the emotional repercussions of that scene, she was able to relive it purely from the sexual perspective and she felt her sex grow warm and slick. Reaching down, between her legs, she caressed the slippery flesh of her labia, parting the folds so that the bubbling water could play against her clitoris and the secret entrance to her body.

By wriggling slightly, she found she could position herself so that a jet of water sprayed directly onto that hard little nub and she immediately felt it swell and push itself out to greet the kiss of the water.

She began to feel warm little ripples of pleasure radiating through her and her breathing became shallow and more rapid. Opening her legs wider, she rocked her hips back and forth.

Suddenly, the water jets became stronger, harder, as if someone had turned up the intensity of the Jacuzzi. Instead of playing gently over her pleasure-bud, now the spray drummed heavily directly on to it. Within seconds Pamela felt the first waves of ecstasy break over her and she cried out, grabbing at the sides of the bath to stop herself from slipping under the frothing water.

12

Her climax seemed to go on and on, a never-ending stream of sensation which sapped her energy, leaving her feeling limp and exhausted. When, at last, it was over, the intensity of the spray lessened and she closed her legs protectively against the now gentle bubbles.

After a few moments, she opened her eyes and found that Luke was standing beside the bath, watching her. How long had he been there? Her cheeks flamed and she dropped her eyes.

'Here,' he said, offering her his hand, 'I've brought you a towel.'

Forgetting for a moment that she was naked, Pamela took his outstretched hand and climbed out of the water. Luke wrapped the huge, fluffy towel around her body and began to pat her dry. Pam was so surprised that she just stood there, not reacting at all until his hands passed over her breasts and stomach.

'I can manage, thank you,' she said, her voice shaking, when she had meant it to be cool.

'I'm sure you can,' Luke assured her smoothly.

Pulling the towel gently off her shoulders, he replaced it with a pale green towelling robe which he belted round her waist for her. Their eyes met and held and Pamela sucked in her breath. She could see compassion in the depths of his eyes and something else, something very like . . . understanding. In that instant she moderated her hastily-made opinion of him. There was warmth in his gaze and she gained the distinct impression that here was a man who actually *liked* women.

He grinned at her suddenly, dispelling the feeling and Pamela felt foolish. He looked like Jack-the-lad again, with about as much perception of her needs as the plastic vibrator Tiffany had given her for her birthday. Could it be that she was projecting her own needs on to him, trying to see empathy in a man where there was none?

'Dinner is in twenty-five minutes,' he said matter-of-factly. 'Why don't you go and dry off in your room?'

His smile was gentle now, but vaguely amused, and Pamela felt her face grow warm again. Watching him walk away, she mused that he must have known what had happened to her in the Jacuzzi. Indeed, it must have been he who turned up the power at the crucial moment. It was almost as if she was supposed to have climaxed, as if he had left her for just long enough for it to happen.

Making her way slowly back to her room, she remembered that Luke had suggested the Jacuzzi was a good place to wind down quickly. She smiled wryly to herself. Well, she certainly felt more relaxed now than she had when she arrived!

'What the hell is this place?' she murmured under her breath as she walked along the opulently decorated corridor which led to her room. As she reached her door she felt a smile spread across her face. She had a feeling that her question would soon be answered. And that finding out was going to be a hell of a lot of fun!

Chapter Two

JEFF LEWIS SAT at his desk and stared at the photograph of his wife he kept there. When Pamela told him she was going away to 'think things over' he hadn't really taken it in, hadn't really considered that she might actually leave him.

She knew about him and Dena. That was the stark fact – she knew and she was hurt. She might well leave him. His shoulders slumped as it hit him properly for the first time. God, he didn't want that! What had he been thinking of? Risking his marriage for a cheap thrill . . .

Pam was right, he hadn't allowed himself time to think of anything lately. Just work. No time to analyse feelings or take the trouble to cherish Pamela – or himself. It wouldn't have been so bad if she hadn't understood; if she'd cried and railed against him, called him a shit and thrown his stuff out of the door, maybe he'd feel better. Instead

15

she'd looked at him with those big, disappointed eyes and told him that she understood why he had been tempted, that she felt it would be best if she went away while they both thought things over. And all the while she'd been so bloody calm, so fucking *understanding*, and for the first time in his life he'd felt as though he might hit her.

Jeff felt guilty. What right did he have to expect histrionics from Pamela just because that would make him feel better? Maybe that was what she meant when she accused him of not taking responsibility for his own behaviour. Did she know how low, how ashamed he felt right now?

The door opened and he looked up hopefully, not realising until he saw Dena how much he had wanted it to be Pamela walking through the door.

'Hi, Jeff – sorry I'm late. Fancy a coffee?'

'Yeah – thanks,' he mumbled, watching her as she hung up her coat and went over to the kettle.

Under her raincoat she was wearing a pink tube of a thing which clung to her generous curves and rode up her thighs as she walked. It struck him, suddenly, that Dena's clothes had grown increasingly tighter and skimpier as the weeks had passed. As he watched, she bent over to find the sugar in the cupboard and her skirt rose right up the backs of her legs, revealing the fact that she wasn't wearing panties.

Jeff had an instant erection and he swallowed, hard. How the hell was he supposed to feel remorseful about his affair when Dena's pink sex

16

was beckoning him from across the room? Agitated, Jeff laid Pamela's photograph face down and stood up. He could tell by the way Dena tensed that she knew he had seen her deliberate come-on and was ready to act upon it. As he approached, he saw that she leaned a little more heavily against the draining board, shifting her feet in their ridiculously high heels as if bracing herself.

Neither spoke, there was no sound in the room except the slight heaviness of their breathing and the distant drone of an earth mover in the compound next door. Jeff could feel the slight vibration caused by the machine rumble through the floor as he positioned himself behind Dena and unzipped his fly. His fingers trembled as he unrolled a condom.

She was ready for him, her plump, pink labia swollen and moist, parting eagerly as he nudged at her entrance with the tip of his cock. Jeff marvelled that he hadn't even had to speak to her, never mind touch her. She was like every man's walking fantasy – ever ready, ever willing. He wasn't made of stone, for God's sake – how could any flesh and blood man be expected to resist such temptation?

He sank into her with a groan, feeling her silky, cleated passage fold around his shaft, drawing him in, welcoming him. Ignoring the image of Pamela which was still at the forefront of his mind, Jeff closed his eyes and began to pump his hips back and forth, bracing his hands on the draining board either side of Dena's body.

Within minutes it was over. Slumping over Dena's broad, hot back, Jeff realised that she was working her own fingers back and forth over her clitoris, trying frantically to catch up with him. This evidence that he was probably as lousy a lover as he was a husband depressed him, though that did not stop him from gripping her by the hips and making the most of the ripples along her vaginal walls as she came.

Now it was all over the excitement drained away quickly, leaving Jeff feeling empty and ashamed. When, at last, he withdrew and began to straighten his clothes, he was embarrassed to realise there were tears on his cheeks. Turning away from Dena so that she wouldn't see, he drew the air in through his nose and held it in his lungs for several seconds as he struggled to control himself.

'Pamela knows about us,' he said when he could trust his voice to remain steady.

Turning towards Dena he saw the dismay which she quickly hid.

'How the hell did she find out? You didn't tell her, did you?'

Jeff stared at her. Her soft, dark hair was tousled and she pushed it off her forehead impatiently. It had never occurred to him to fancy her until a few weeks ago. She was nice enough, sexy too, in a rather obvious, overblown style. But if he was to be brutally honest with himself he would have to say that it was her sheer availability which had attracted him most.

Dena and Pamela had been friends long before Jeff had come on to the scene. It had been Pamela who suggested that he should offer Dena a job when she was made redundant. Briefly, he wondered which of them was guilty of the greatest betrayal – the 'best' friend or the husband? Suddenly he felt horribly, unutterably weary.

'She saw us. The other night when we were working late. She came to the office and she saw us and . . .' He trailed off as he saw Dena's white face.

'Oh God – poor Pamela!' she whispered. 'What did she say?'

'Not a lot. She's gone away for a while – some health farm her sister goes to.'

'Will she be coming back?'

Jeff shrugged and Dena's face flooded with alarm.

'Hey, Jeff, this was supposed to be a bit of fun . . . I never intended for Pamela to get hurt!'

'And you think I did?'

'No, of course not! I . . . I just wanted to be sure where I stand . . . if Pam doesn't come back.'

Jeff looked at her and was assailed by a sudden dislike.

'Don't worry, Dena,' he snapped, 'I won't expect you to move in with me or anything like that. I mean, Christ, let's not get into the realms of commitment here!'

Dena shifted uncomfortably and her eyes slid away from his.

'So – do we call it a day, or what?' she mumbled with an attempt at nonchalance which didn't quite work.

'I think we'd better, don't you? Rather like shutting the proverbial stable door?'

'Right. Er . . . what about my job? I mean . . . we will be able to go on working together, won't we? You're not going to sack me or anything?'

Jeff sighed heavily and picked up his jacket. 'And have you take me to a tribunal? What do you take me for?'

Dena looked hurt. 'I'd never do that! Let's not be bitter, Jeff, please. After all, we did have some fun, didn't we?'

She dimpled at him and Jeff felt himself softening towards her. It wasn't fair to lay all the blame at her door – it was his marriage which had been on the line.

'We did. Just do me a favour, Dena.'

'What's that?'

'Go home and change into something more suitable for work.'

He smiled ruefully at her and slipped through the door, suddenly desperate for some space to himself.

Pamela stretched luxuriously and winced as some rough skin on her heel snagged against the silk sheets. Though their image was romantic, silk sheets, in reality, were only for those with pampered skin, she concluded. She'd have to use some of that expensive softening lotion she had

20

spied in the bathroom before she went to bed last night!

Rising slowly, she went through to the bathroom and turned on the taps. As she waited for the bath to fill, Pamela thought back over the time she had spent at dinner the evening before.

Her fellow guests were a mixed bunch. Both male and female, they had all looked up as she entered the dining-room and nodded politely to her before turning their attention back to their meals. Pamela had been seated with a tall, ebony-skinned girl who introduced herself as Casey, holding out her hand in greeting. Pam took the long, elegant fingers in her own and marvelled at the inch-long red talons on the other girl's hands.

'Gorgeous, aren't they?' Casey drawled in a Southern American accent which was as thick as treacle. 'The manicurist here is an artist!'

'Have you been here long?' Pamela had asked, aware as she did so that she sounded awfully prissy.

'A few days. My husband pays for me to fly over every six months to iron out the creases.' Casey gave her a curious, cat-like smile. 'Gives us both a break from each other. And, of course, it gets me outta the way for a while – know what I mean?'

'You mean . . .?'

'Sure, honey. Monogamy can be death to a marriage, don't you think?'

'Well, I . . . I've always thought—'

'Honey,' Casey said huskily, leaning over the table and folding one elegantly manicured hand over Pamela's, 'let me give you some advice. While you're at Elysium Hall, don't think, just *feel*. You'll enjoy your stay here much more if you let yourself go with the flow.'

Pamela smiled now as she stepped into her bath and thought how she had grown to like the beautiful Afro-American as they had eaten together. Casey might be unconventional, but she had a wicked sense of humour and it soon became clear that she was willing to be friendly. After she had finished the delicious seafood pastry, Pamela had booked herself a manicure and arranged to meet Casey for morning coffee in the conservatory at ten.

It was almost nine-thirty now, but Pamela found she simply could not force herself to hurry. Smoothing a fine layer of Estée Lauder's *Beautiful* body lotion all over her naked form, she felt decadent, deliciously self-indulgent. Her skin was soft and warm from her bath, still slightly damp, and the smooth cream was quickly absorbed, wrapping her in its gentle perfume.

There was a fresh robe hanging on the back of her door and she slipped her arms in and belted it. There was something rather liberating about not having to choose something suitable to wear each day – at Elysium Hall she need wear nothing but a towelling gown over her undies.

On her way downstairs to the conservatory, Pamela passed Luke in the corridor. He smiled at her and she found herself responding as if to an old friend. The ambiance of this place must be getting to her already, she mused, pushing open the swing doors.

Inside the large, hexagonal shaped conservatory, the air was warm and humid. Waiters passed discreetly amongst the scattered loungers where various people were taking a late breakfast, reading the newspapers, or merely relaxing in the early summer sunshine which was streaming through the glass dome of the conservatory roof. Pamela spotted Casey at the far side of the room, looking very colourful in a brightly patterned kaftan, her long black hair hidden beneath a matching silk turban. Pamela smiled as the other girl waved in greeting.

'Hi, Pam! How are you today?'

'I'm fine thanks, Casey – and you?'

Casey rolled her eyes so that the whites shone against the ebony sheen of her skin.

'It gets better by the minute!' She laughed. 'See that waiter over there? The one with the cute little buns? Honey, have I got plans for him!'

Pamela looked over to where a well-built young man with long, curly brown hair drawn back into a pony-tail was serving a middle-aged woman and her friend. As she looked, he turned his head and smiled at Casey, who waggled her fingers coyly at him and laughed again.

'Don't look so shocked, Pammie – loosen up! Take it from me – that guy has a tongue with re-al talent, know what I mean?'

'You – you mean he . . . that you . . .'

Pam was lost for words, yet she had to admit, she was more fascinated than appalled. Her reaction surprised her – she had never thought of herself as being particularly liberated when it came to casual sex. She was beginning to realise, though, that anything might be possible in this strange place.

A waiter appeared at their table then and she ordered herself coffee and croissants and a copy of *Vogue*. Casey, she noticed, was reading *GQ*.

'I like to know how their little minds work, honey,' she said wickedly as she saw Pamela looking.

Pam laughed.

'Casey, you really are quite incorrigible!'

'You betcha! Hey – looks like Amanda's on her way over.'

Pamela turned and saw that Casey was right – Amanda was making a beeline for their table.

'Good morning, ladies,' she said brightly, flashing a wide smile, straight from a toothpaste ad. 'I've put you down for a massage with Luke in an hour or so, Pamela, so don't disappear, will you? And go easy on the croissants – you don't want a full stomach. As for you Casey—'

'Honey, don't you worry about me, I have plans of my own.'

Amanda raised her eyebrows as she followed Casey's gaze across the conservatory to where the young man on whom she had her eye was clearing a recently abandoned table.

'I see. Well, Casey, Rob is okay, but leave him with some energy left over for our other ladies, right?'

The two girls laughed together as if at some private joke, leaving Pamela intrigued. Were all the men here available for extra-curricular duties? She looked around her with renewed interest, seeing them all through new eyes. There was the slender Hispanic waiter who had served her for dinner. As Pamela watched, he bent over the woman for whom he was pouring coffee and whispered something in her ear. The woman, a petite brunette with immaculate make-up and a monied air, smiled at him conspiratorially and touched his hand.

Pamela shivered as she considered the possibilities. What of Luke – was he available for more intimate 'treatments' too? She brought herself up short – what was she thinking of? She hadn't come here with the intention of being unfaithful to Jeff. Even thinking about it made her feel uncomfortable – it seemed too much like a kind of revenge fantasy for his affair with Dena.

She jumped as her breakfast arrived, smiling guiltily at the impassive waiter. He winked at her cheekily and Pamela grinned. What the hell – there was no harm in looking!

'Have a nice day,' Amanda said, then she left them, marking them off on her clipboard.

'You're looking real thoughtful, Pam,' Casey said as she watched Pamela dividing her croissant into two crumbly halves. 'Want to share your troubles with me?'

Pamela smiled self-consciously. 'I'm sorry, Casey, I was miles away.'

'I could see that! Just where did you go, if you don't mind my asking, that is?'

Pamela looked at the other girl consideringly. To her surprise she found that she wanted to confide in her, and she had a feeling that she would be sympathetic, despite their differing views on marriage and monogamy.

'Of course I don't mind. I was wondering what Jeff was doing right now. He's my husband.'

'Won't he be taking advantage of your absence?' Casey said, an edge of cynicism to her voice.

Pamela sighed. 'Probably. I was just wondering if he'd even noticed that I'm not there.'

'Hey – is he a blind man or what?'

Pamela smiled weakly. 'He might just as well be when he's around me,' she muttered. 'Oh, I don't know. I suppose . . . well, I suppose I miss him.' To her horror, one fat tear brimmed in each eye and fell on to her tightly clasped hands. 'I'm sorry, Casey. How very silly of me!'

'You cry, girl – let it all out. Here—' she passed Pamela a tiny, lace-trimmed handkerchief— 'have a good blow! Is he worth crying over, this husband of yours?'

'I used to think so.'

'So what happened?'

Pamela told her everything and Casey listened without interrupting. When Pamela had finished, she raised her finely shaped eyebrows and looked at her steadily.

'Honey, do you really want to bust up your marriage over one little old slip?'

Pamela looked at her indignantly. 'That's not the point, is it? It isn't so much that Jeff was . . . was . . . you know, with Dena. He betrayed my trust. I don't think things could ever be the same again.'

Casey poured more coffee and handed Pamela a cup. 'Seems to me that you weren't happy with the way things were before anyhow. Maybe this could be a chance for you both to start over – make something new.'

'Do you think so?'

Casey shrugged her elegant shoulders. 'Doesn't much matter what I think. It's how you *feel* that counts.'

Pamela sipped her coffee thoughtfully, mulling over Casey's words. It all sounded so simple, using the other girl's logic. Yet she was still nursing too much hurt to let it go completely.

'Looks like Rob's ready for me.' Casey stood and stretched her long, lithe body upward. Pamela caught a waft of her perfume and she breathed it in, trying to identify the exotic, floral fragrance. 'I'll meet up with you later, Pam honey. If I were you, I wouldn't even try to think for a few days. You give yourself over to Luke's capable hands and find out what *you* like, before you even start to consider how your husband fits in. See you later!'

27

Pamela watched her as she strolled across the conservatory, admiring her loose-limbed, confident walk. Casey seemed so *together* somehow, Pamela could not help but envy her self-confidence. What she had said struck a chord with Pamela. It seemed to her that Casey had talked a lot of sense and that her advice might well be worth heeding.

Abandoning her half eaten breakfast, Pamela lay back on her lounger and closed her eyes. Somewhere close by she could hear a woman and a man laughing together. The sound was low, intimate, and it made something stir restlessly in the pit of her stomach. Intimacy, that was what she and Jeff had lost. She couldn't imagine that he had found that particular emotion with Dena, of all people.

Quickly, Pamela cut off that line of thought. Casey was right – she should be concentrating on herself and only herself while she was here. What was the point of dwelling on things she couldn't change? Resolutely, she made herself relax and empty her mind of all such self-destructive thoughts. Gradually, the sounds around her faded so that they seemed to be coming from far away, and within a few minutes she had slipped into a light doze.

. . . In her dreams she could see a couple standing in a garden. She realised that they looked exactly like the couple portrayed on the mural in the swimming area – he standing, she kneeling at his feet, her lips stretched wide around his distended penis. It was the same, and yet different. The garden was *her* garden, at home – she could even see the yellow roses that Jeff had planted for her on their first wedding anniversary.

The woman was a stranger to her – blonde with a model-perfect figure. She was wearing some kind of body-suit, flesh-coloured and clinging, nothing else. Pamela could see her pale pink nipples pushing against the stretched fabric and the distortion caused by the blonde fur on her pubis.

She seemed to be enjoying fellating the man for her eyes were closed as if in ecstasy and her cheeks bulged with each inward thrust. Pamela could see her tongue, pink and wet, lapping greedily at the clear pre-emission and she envied her her prowess.

It came as no surprise to recognise the man. Jeff's head was arched back and his face had the set, intense expression that it always had in the moments before he came. Pamela smiled. She was glad that he was enjoying what the girl was doing to him. Strangely, she felt no jealousy, and she knew that he was doing this with her knowledge, her permission.

'Jeff!' she called, gently, from where she was standing by the back door.

His head turned slightly and their eyes met. He knew, then, that she was watching. Perhaps they had planned this scene together earlier. He smiled at her, tenderly, his eyes signalling his love for her. Then he shuddered and Pamela knew that his seed was pumping along his shaft, towards the girl's open mouth.

Pamela felt the throb of her own sex as she watched the girl swallow greedily, her pale throat convulsing as burst after burst of fluid came into her mouth. There was too much – it seeped between her lips and ran down her chin, trickling on to her neck and breasts.

Jeff groaned and tangled his fingers in the girl's hair as it came to an end. Gently, he urged her to stand and turned her towards Pamela. The girl smiled happily, it seemed to Pamela. Without hesitation, she approached them, her eyes on the girl's full, pink lips, smeared with Jeff's semen.

In her dream, Pamela put her hands on the girl's shoulders and kissed her, deeply, licking at the insides of her cheeks, drinking in her husband's fluid. She could feel the girl's breasts pressing softly against her own and she dropped her head to kiss each sweet crest. God, how she wanted her!

The girl's slender arms came around Pamela's body, urging her down, on to the grass. Jeff's hand was on her shoulder, shaking her gently. She could hear him calling to her.

'Pamela? Pamela . . .?'

She frowned. Something was wrong – that wasn't Jeff's voice! Slowly, she opened eyes that felt as though they had been glued together. Sure enough, the eyes level with hers were blue, not light brown like Jeff's.

'Pamela – are you with us now?'

'Luke!'

He straightened, looking at her curiously. 'I think you must have been having rather an interesting dream,' he said. 'It was a shame to wake you!'

Pamela's cheeks flamed. Had she given away by some word or gesture exactly what she had been doing in her dream? She would be mortified if this beautiful young man could see inside her mind and recognise her most intimate fantasies! She frowned. Was making love with another woman really one of her fantasies?

'This is Dirk,' Luke was saying and for the first time Pamela realised that he wasn't alone. The man with him was as dark and swarthy as Luke was fair, and aesthetically the two of them provided a perfect foil for each other.

'Um, hello,' Pamela said, still drowsy.

'Dirk is going to help me with your massage – if that's all right with you?'

Pamela gaped. Was it all right with her? She wasn't sure that giving herself over to the ministrations of two masseurs was wise but she felt herself nodding. Luke smiled.

'Good. As it's such a lovely day, we thought we'd go down to the lake. Come.'

He held out his hand to her and Pamela reluctantly took it. They were taking her to the lake? For a *massage*? She considered changing her mind, but then she thought, for the second time that day – what the hell? Despite her initial wariness of him, she trusted Luke. And Dirk was so darkly handsome, she had a feeling it might prove to be a rather rewarding experience to be the object of both their attentions at once.

Smiling, she linked one arm through each of theirs and headed out into the sunshine.

Chapter Three

IT WAS HOT in the garden, the bright August sunshine streaming from a cloudless sky, tinting the lush green grass with a golden glow.

'Shall we walk through the rose garden?' Luke asked.

Pamela shook her head. Roses reminded her of Jeff, and the last thing she wanted right now was to think of him.

'I'd rather not.'

'Okay – we'll go this way.'

Luke led them along a narrow pathway which meandered along the edge of the rolling lawns before disappearing into a copse. It was shady under the trees, the air rich and loamy, and Pamela drew it deeply into her lungs.

'Pleased to get out in the fresh air?' Luke asked her.

She smiled. 'Yes. I was brought up on a farm, in Devon. I miss the space, living in a city.'

As she spoke she realised that this hadn't occurred to her before. When she and Jeff had bought a house together, they had only looked at starter homes in the city centre. Obviously, it was important to be near his business and her work, but there were many pretty little villages only a short drive away. Why hadn't they looked at those?

'This is rather a . . . special place, isn't it?' she said wistfully. 'My sister said it would be.'

'Your sister?'

'Tiffany Reynolds. She comes here regularly with my brother-in-law, Mick. Maybe you know them?'

She caught the look Luke passed over her head to Dirk and she frowned. For a moment he seemed to be about to say something about the couple, but in the event all he said was, 'We both know Mick and Tiffany.'

Dirk was carrying a large, sports-type holdall which appeared to be heavy, for he kept switching it from one hand to the other as he walked. So far he hadn't said a word, but when Pamela caught his eye, he smiled, an open, friendly smile which reassured her.

As they stepped out into the sunlight again, Pamela saw the lake spreading out in front of them and her step faltered. It was vast, dotted with some half a dozen small islands. Neatly mown grass bordered it and there were several benches and picnic tables scattered about. Amongst the reeds, a rowing boat lay moored, bobbing gently up and down on the breeze-blown waves. As they watched, a flock of swans descended from the clear blue sky, landing on the surface of the water with such precision that they barely caused a ripple.

'Oh, it's beautiful!' Pamela gasped. 'I don't think I've ever seen so many swans in one place before.'

'They nest on the islands over there,' Luke explained proudly. 'We've increased the swan population by half in the past two years.'

When they had found a sheltered spot, Dirk unzipped the holdall and spread a blanket on the ground which he covered with a towel.

'If you lie this way, you'll be able to watch the swans during the massage.'

It was the first time Dirk had spoken and Pamela smiled at him, liking the sound of his voice. It was soft, not wimpish, but deep and sensitive. Loosening her robe, she lay on her stomach on the towel and folded her arms beneath her chin. Gentle hands eased her robe off her shoulders so that her arms were, effectively, pinned to her sides.

Pamela felt a slight shiver of anticipation. She pictured herself, restrained lightly by the sleeves of her robe, lying face down on the tartan rug, the two men kneeling on the grass either side of her. Strong fingers began to knead at the tense muscles in the back of her neck and shoulders and she sighed. She had never been touched in such an intimate way by anyone other than her husband, or her sister who used to massage her neck when she had a migraine.

Did Luke and Dirk find her attractive, or was she effectively invisible to them, her massage simply one of many they had to perform today – routine?

Closing her eyes the better to concentrate on the delicious, self-indulgent sensations running through her, Pamela concluded that none of it mattered, really. This was for her, for her pleasure alone. These men were here purely to give her pleasure. She didn't have to worry about holding her stomach in, or whether her bottom looked pleasing to them. There was no need to even consider their feelings, or whether either of them was enjoying himself. It didn't even matter that she didn't know which one was currently touching her. It was all for her and her alone.

Pamela found this notion powerfully liberating. Carrying it through to its logical conclusion, she wondered just how far they would be prepared to go? Casey was obviously deeply involved with Rob, sexually. Would Luke and Dirk be happy to perform the same service for her?

She smiled at herself for even thinking of such a preposterous idea, knowing that she would be outraged should fantasy merge with fact. That did not stop her from imagining how it would be if the strong, skilful fingers now kneading either side of her spine were to edge further round her body, to mould and caress her breasts which were squashed against the towelling-covered blanket.

'Is that good?'

It was Luke who spoke, his voice low and mellifluous, and Pamela realised that she must have sighed aloud.

'Mmm,' she mumbled, aware that a dull flush had crept into her cheeks at the thought of where her mind had taken her.

'You're very tense – I'm going to get Dirk to concentrate on the lower half of your body while I work on these knots in your back.'

Pam hardly registered what he said, she was too focused on the language he was speaking with his hands. As he kneaded and manipulated the muscles in her back, she could feel all the tension draining away so that she felt as though she was floating, light as a feather.

Dirk cradled one of her feet in his hands and began to rub the sole with his thumbs. Surprisingly, it didn't tickle, and after a few minutes, Pamela felt as though her entire body was gradually being suffused with warmth. The oil the men were using was rich and heavy, its fragrance redolent of bergamot and cloves. Combined with the sweet-sharp tang of the newly mown grass and the faint scent of the rose garden carried on the gentle breeze, it provided an almost drugging effect on the senses.

Pamela felt quite drowsy as the two men worked silently on her body, their movements soothingly synchronised in order to give her the greatest pleasure. She had never had a massage before and, sleepily, she wondered why. Certainly she had never dreamt it would be quite so . . . *good*.

She was a little embarrassed, and faintly amused, to realise that it was turning her on, her recalcitrant imagination still running away with her. Dirk's fingers were edging up her legs now, stroking the fragile skin at the backs of her knees and sinking slightly into the fleshier thighs. Pamela had to fight the instinct to let them fall apart, clenching her bottom cheeks so that she would not disgrace herself.

How could they not notice that she was becoming aroused? Gritting her teeth as Luke's clever fingers found the undeniably erogenous circle of her waist, she kept her eyes tightly closed for fear that her pupils had enlarged and they would be able to read the desire in her eyes.

It was all she could do not to groan aloud with frustration as, just before Dirk reached her clenched buttocks, he changed direction and stroked softly back down the backs of her legs. Shortly afterwards, Luke also stopped what he was doing, leaving Pamela feeling strangely bereft.

'Would you like some champagne?' he asked her as he covered her shoulders with her robe.

'Champagne?'

Pamela was so taken aback by the unexpected question that she forgot to avoid his eye and turned her flushed face towards him.

'You look hot,' he said, innocently enough. 'The bottle has been on ice.'

Sitting up on the rug, Pamela saw that Dirk had unzipped the holdall to reveal a large bottle of

Bollinger complete with ice-bucket. He smiled disarmingly at her and held out a glass.

As she took it, their fingertips accidentally touched and Pamela felt an unexpected *frisson* as she felt the warmth of his skin. Their eyes met and she was startled to realise that, far from being unaffected by what he was doing to her, Dirk's eyes mirrored her own arousal. Dropping her gaze to his trackpants, she saw the unmistakable stretching of the fabric across his crotch and felt a fresh rush of moisture between her thighs. She looked away quickly, confused by the strength of her feelings.

She concentrated on watching the bubbles fight to escape her glass as he filled it. This was the very first time since her marriage that she had seriously desired another man. And yet she could not claim to know this man at all, indeed she had barely exchanged half a dozen words with him. It wasn't like her – she didn't normally have these impetuous, inconvenient attacks of lust – it wasn't like her at all.

As if sensing her confusion, Luke drew her attention to the rowing boat nestling amongst the reeds at the edge of the lake.

'It's such a lovely day – perhaps you'd like Dirk to row you round the lake? It's marvellously peaceful out there on the water.'

Pamela gazed out across the tranquil lake and was surprised to find that Luke had pinpointed exactly what she wanted to do with the rest of her morning. Turning, she smiled at him. 'A little too peaceful, I think – after that massage I could well fall asleep!'

Luke smiled enigmatically. 'Feel free. Though I've never known Dirk to lose anyone yet.'

Sensing Dirk's eyes on her, Pamela glanced across at him, aware that she was reluctant to meet his look. He was gazing steadily at her, his eyes half closed, his square, strong-boned face impassive. Something in her stomach dipped, then soared. She could not remember feeling quite the same way since she was a teenager.

'I'll leave you two to it,' Luke said, draining his glass. 'Take the bottle on to the boat. I'll help you get underway.'

'Aren't you coming too?' Pamela asked, alarmed at the thought of being totally alone on the lake with Dirk.

Luke smiled again. 'It's a very small boat,' he said. 'Besides, I have an aerobics class to teach in half an hour. Dirk will take good care of you.'

'Oh.'

Pamela could think of nothing else of say. It seemed that her schedule had been predetermined for her. As Tiffany – and, later, Casey – had told her, at Elysium Hall there was no need to think. No call for rationalisation or analysis. Everything was organised for the guests, right down to the last meticulous detail.

Even now it seemed that all she was required to do was wait while the two men untied the boat, wading out into the lake to free the mooring which had become caught underneath it. When

40

they were ready, Dirk jumped in and took up the oars while Luke waded back to the bank. There he scooped Pamela up into his arms and carried her, too surprised to protest, to the boat.

Unexpectedly, there were cushions arranged at the bow end of the boat and Pamela was able to make herself comfortable. She giggled as she held her hand over the side and trailed her finger through the cold, clear water.

'I feel like one of those Victorian ladies – minus a parasol,' she said.

Luke raised his eyebrows. 'Next time I'll bring you an appropriate costume!'

Pamela looked down at her bare legs beneath the towelling robe and grinned. 'I don't really look the part, do I?'

'Never mind. Enjoy yourselves. I'll see you later.'

He watched as Dirk began to row, sculling out towards the centre of the lake where the water was deeper. Once she became used to the rocking motion, Pamela leaned back on the cushions and relaxed.

Luke was right, it was peaceful on the water. The sun was warm, though not so hot as to be uncomfortable. There was no one else about to witness the incongruous sight of a woman in her dressing gown being rowed across the lake in broad daylight, and Pamela soon decided she would not care even if there was.

Dirk was restful company. Though he didn't say a word, his silence was not taciturn. Rather he

41

seemed to sense her need for solitude and was sensitive enough not to intrude upon it. Therefore it came as a shock when, after about half an hour, he said softly, 'I'll tether the boat to the jetty on the island there and you can have that nap you've been coveting.'

Pam started, then smiled. 'Is it that obvious?'

'You've been struggling to stay awake.'

'Perhaps you and Luke relaxed me a little too much,' she admitted.

Dirk merely smiled and set a course for one of the larger islands in the lake. Watching him surreptitiously from beneath her lashes, Pamela admired the play of the muscles in his arms and shoulders as he pulled on the oars. He was wearing a white singlet which was cut away at the shoulders, showing off his tan. Pamela could see a fine film of sweat lying on his skin, forming a sheen in the sunshine. He was so close she could smell the faint, intimate scent of it and she licked her lips, aware that her mouth had grown dry.

Dirk's eyes followed the motion and for one breathless moment, Pamela thought he was going to reach for her. She didn't know whether to be relieved or disappointed when he said gently, 'Why don't you relax while I tie up the boat? I'll leave you for a few minutes while I check on some work we've been doing on the island and you can doze in the sunshine.'

She nodded, watching him through half-closed eyes as he climbed out of the boat and secured it at a mooring post. Looking back at her once, over his shoulder, he flashed her a grin which, she was convinced, was tinged with mischief before disappearing into the undergrowth.

Pamela stretched luxuriously and made herself more comfortable on the cushions. Turning over, on to her stomach, she pillowed her head on her folded arms and swept her eyes across the lake, taking in the view of the Hall, rising up majestically from amongst the extensive gardens, its many-paned windows glinting mysteriously in the sunlight. It was like a fairytale place, not quite real.

A sound punctured the stillness and Pamela's head swivelled, searching for its source. A woman's giggle, low and seductive, somewhere close. There was another island, almost parallel to the one where they had moored, and Pamela's eyes were drawn to where a blanket had been spread on the ground at the edge of the lake.

There was a woman lying on the blanket. Pam judged her to be in her late forties, with short dark hair cut close to her head, a style which emphasised her elfin features. She remembered seeing her at dinner the evening before, dining with an elegantly dressed, grey-haired man who Pamela had assumed was her husband.

It certainly wasn't her husband who was slowly stripping off her clothes now! Pamela watched, appalled by her own voyeurism, but unable to drag her eyes away as the woman's lithe, white body was revealed. She was too far away to see the expression on her face, but she could see from the way she held herself, with a kind of expectant tension, that the woman was highly aroused.

Pamela felt an answering desire stirring in her own belly and she shifted on her cushions, aware that she was witnessing what should be a most intimate and private moment. The man who was now casting aside the last of the woman's underwear was young and tanned with broad, wide shoulders beneath his dark-coloured T-shirt. Pam shivered as she watched him dip his head to nuzzle the soft hair where the woman's thighs met.

God, how lascivious the scene looked! Pamela moistened her lips, with an increasing sense of participating in something illicit, exciting. Leaning back on her elbows, the woman threw back her head, the white arc of her throat shining in the bright sunlight.

'Oh, that's *so-o* good!' she cried, her voice, clear as a bell, carried over the tranquil water to where Pamela was listening.

Pamela closed her eyes for an instant as a wave of sheer empathic lust washed over her. She could imagine so vividly how the unknown man's lips would feel against the other woman's vulva as he slowly, tantalisingly, worked his way inward to the soft inner lips. Her labia would be swollen in anticipation, the skin tingling, slick with moisture. His tongue would tease along the grooves of her most intimate flesh, drawing out her hardening clitoris until it had grown firm and shiny as a small bead . . .

'Yes ... oh yes!' The woman cried out, her voice rising.

Pamela could feel a pulse flutter into life between her legs as she opened her eyes and saw that the woman had now wrapped her long legs around the young man's shoulders and his face was buried between her thighs. The woman's arms were flung up above her head and she was writhing, on the verge of orgasm.

The boat dipped slightly and Pamela knew without turning round that Dirk had rejoined her. Had she not been so aroused by the sight, she might have been embarrassed to have been caught watching the erotic scene across the lake. She knew that Dirk would immediately see what had transfixed her and she held her breath as he came closer.

Without turning her head, she sensed his nearness. The sharp salt-tang of his skin and the healthy, animal warmth which emanated from his body acted as a spur to her senses and she sighed audibly.

It was inevitable that he should touch her, inevitable that the first contact of his skin with hers would cause her to sink against the cushions, assailed by a sudden, unaccustomed weakness. Across the lake, the sounds of the other woman's orgasm floated on the breeze, but Pamela was no longer interested. Her concerns were now more immediate, closer to home.

Without a word, Dirk ran his fingertips lightly up her leg to the parting of her robe. He hesitated there for a moment, as if assessing her reaction. Pamela did not dare to raise her eyes to his, and kept her gaze firmly on his tanned fingers, sprinkled with sparse, black hairs, which hovered at her inner thigh. With a soft groan of surrender, she slid her bottom down the cushions, so that Dirk's hand was caught beneath the hem of the towelling robe. It was an invitation so blatant, she might just as well have spoken her need aloud.

Pamela closed her eyes as Dirk's fingertips brushed against the silky hair of her mons. Even that delicate touch sent ripples of delight travelling up towards the core of her. It was as if, by watching the other couple, she had bypassed her usual need for extensive foreplay, and she was eager for him to touch her where the small pulse throbbed insistently, demanding attention.

Dirk did not disappoint her. She gasped as his whole palm covered her vulva, his fingers curling into the soft, wet flesh inside, causing a delicious spasm to pass through her. His other arm came around her shoulders, holding her as he moved his body up the boat and spread his length alongside her.

The boat rocked alarmingly, yet Pamela barely noticed. She felt as if she was standing on the edge of a precipice, her whole body poised to leap into a void. As Dirk began to stroke delicately along the slippery channels of her sex, she clung to him, finding the exquisite sensations he caused almost too much to bear.

His warm, firm lips brushed lightly across her

forehead, as if to reassure her. At the same time, his middle finger dipped into the well of her arousal, scooping up the honeyed moisture and working it up to the small nub of her clitoris.

Pamela shuddered at the first touch of his fingers there, knowing that it would not take much to tip her over the edge. Dirk circled his fingerpad round and round, slowly at first, but with the perfect, unbroken rhythm that she loved. How could he have found this out about her at once? she marvelled as he began to increase the speed and the pressure.

Behind her closed eyelids, Pamela relived the scene she had witnessed across the lake, knowing how the other woman had felt as the man had sucked and licked at her. Everything seemed to have shifted into sharper focus. The scent of male skin with its hint of arousal; the strength of the arm holding her; the faint, sweet brush of his breath against her cheek.

The sun was hot on her face and neck and her exposed sex. She wondered if, somewhere close, she, in her turn, was being spied upon. The idea both appalled and thrilled her and it was this that provided the final spur to her desire.

With a small, strangled cry, Pamela arched her back and bore down on Dirk's fingers, her breath coming in short, sharp bursts as the sensations radiated through her. Dirk kept up the pressure until the tenor of her cry changed from ecstasy to mild protest, then he cupped her still throbbing sex in his palm and held it.

At last, as her breathing slowed and her legs stopped shaking, he removed his hand before drawing the two sides of her robe together. Slowly, reluctantly, Pamela opened her eyes.

Dirk smiled at her, a friendly, gentle smile, before moving down to the seat and picking up the oars.

'Time to get back,' he said matter-of-factly.

Pamela's eyes fell irresistibly to the unmistakable bulge in his shorts. Its presence reassured her – how awful if he had remained totally unmoved by her! Catching her eye, Dirk smiled again.

'Later?' he said.

Pamela bit her lip, knowing her eyes were overbright as she thought of the possibilities. Then she nodded. Why not?

'Later,' she murmured, and smiled.

Chapter Four

JEFF ROLLED OVER in the big double bed and encountered the white cotton nightie that Pamela had worn the night before she left. Catching the lingering scent of her perfume, he buried his face in the crisp fabric and breathed in deeply, closing his eyes as he remembered how she looked when she was inside it.

'Do you like it?' she had asked him anxiously the first time she wore it. 'It's not too old-maidish is it?'

Jeff had eyed her lasciviously, enjoying the way the outwardly demure garment hid and yet exposed her lovely body. It clung faithfully to her breasts and hips, flaring gently across her stomach before falling in delicate folds to her ankles. He remembered that there was something rather alluring about the sight of her pale pink feet peeping from beneath the expanse of fabric.

As she moved across the light shed by the

bedside lamp, her whole body had been suddenly outlined beneath the white cotton, making him catch his breath.

'It's definitely not old-maidish!' he'd said hoarsely, reaching for her.

They had made love that night as if for the very first time, the pair of them hungry for each other, giving and receiving in equal measure until, finally, they had fallen into the sleep of the exhausted, the pristine white cotton nightie crumpled between them, damp with sweat.

Now Jeff held the abandoned nightdress against his naked body and felt himself harden in response to the memory. Strange how he had forgotten that night until now. They used to be so in love, so utterly *right* for each other – when had it all gone wrong?

He wondered what Pamela was doing now and whether she thought about him at all. She must be lonely at that health farm . . . would she welcome a telephone call from him?

Galvanised by a sudden need to talk to her, Jeff reached for the phone by the bed and tapped out his sister-in-law's number. She knew where Pamela was – surely she'd give him the number? If only he could talk to Pamela, tell her he was missing her, perhaps he could at least begin to bridge the chasm which had opened up between them?

His heart sank as Tiffany's voice came over on the answerphone. Of course – she and Mick would still be in Paris. He would have to wait until the end of the week before he could find out where Pamela was – or wait for her to contact him.

With a groan of pure frustration, he wrapped the lightly scented nightdress around his restless body and tried to sleep.

Casey was waiting for Pamela when she came down for dinner that evening.

'Hey, honey – you look like the cat that had the cream!' Casey laughed as the heat rose in Pamela's cheeks. 'Wow! Looks like you've got a tale to tell.'

'Nonsense,' Pamela replied primly, 'I've just had a very relaxing day, that's all.'

She could tell by Casey's wide grin that she was not fooled for a minute and she toyed with the idea of confiding in her. But confiding what? Despite his enigmatic promise on the boat, Pamela had not seen Dirk since he walked with her back to the house after their trip on the lake. She had spent the rest of the day in a fever of anticipation, wondering when 'later' would be.

At first when she did not see him again she had felt disappointed, then angry. Her pique had quickly turned to relief, which gradually mellowed during the day to a vague, nagging anxiety that she might have made an absolute fool of herself.

'Casey – are all the men terribly promiscuous here?' she blurted.

Casey raised her finely plucked eyebrows.

'Why, not *promiscuous*, Pammie. That's not the right word at all. Adventurous, perhaps?'

Pamela, who was silently berating herself for being so indiscreet, decided she might as well jump in for a penny as for a pound. 'Have you slept with many? Oh God, Casey, what must you think of me? I'm not normally this crass!'

Casey regarded her for a moment, her head held on one side. 'Well,' she said at last, 'I have my moments. I guess something's bothering you, huh? C'mon – tell Auntie Casey all about it.'

The waiter arrived then with the first course and the two women maintained a discreet silence until he had retreated again, his footsteps virtually silent on the soft, red carpet in the dining-room.

Seeing that Casey was still watching her expectantly, Pamela toyed with her seafood cocktail and sighed. 'I think you'd better tell me a little more about Elysium Hall, Casey – I seem to be reading the signals I'm getting all wrong!'

Ignoring her plate, Casey sat back in her seat and sighed happily. 'Elysium Hall is anything you want it to be, hon. If all you want is a relaxing few days in the countryside with good food and a few beauty treatments thrown in, then it will deliver. It's one of the best. If, however, you're looking for a little more *action* – and I'm not talking tennis, or step-aerobic classes here – then that can be arranged too.'

'How do they know what you want?'

Casey smiled enigmatically. 'They're all well

trained. Luke and Amanda are looking after you, right?'

Pamela nodded.

'Well, then they will have devised a programme for you. It would have begun today – does that give you any clues?'

Pamela felt the colour seeping into her cheeks again as she thought of what her 'programme' had entailed. Seeing that Casey was expecting her to tell all, she tried to oblige her.

'I think so. I was taken down to the lake by Luke and Dirk and given a massage. Then Dirk rowed me out to one of the islands, and . . .'

'And something happened to put that fetching glow in your cheeks,' Casey finished for her when she faltered.

Pamela laughed softly. 'Yes.'

Casey attacked her starter now with gusto and the two women waited while their plates were removed.

'So – why the confusion?' Casey said after a few minutes.

Pamela shrugged slightly. 'I . . . it was all very *gentle*, if you know what I mean.'

Casey's eyebrows rose again. 'And you prefer things less gentle?'

'Oh no. I mean . . . oh, Casey, I don't know what I mean! It's just that we didn't . . . you know. Not *together*.'

'And you wanted to.'

'Yes.' Pamela dropped her eyes, shamed by the admission. 'And he knew that. He said . . . he said

53

''Later''. And I thought that he wanted me . . .' She trailed off, feeling quite desolate.

Casey reached across the table, her smooth, dark-skinned hand closing over Pamela's. It felt warm and comforting, and to her surprise, Pamela felt the slightest *frisson* of something familiar stirring in the pit of her stomach. She frowned, keeping her eyes lowered so that Casey wouldn't see the sudden confusion in her eyes and misunderstand it.

'Poor baby! He'll come. If I were you, I'd go up early after dinner.'

Pamela swallowed hard. 'But I shouldn't. I mean . . . it feels too much like I'm trying to get my own back on Jeff. It isn't right.'

Casey squeezed her hand. 'Honey, it's just sex. It has nothing to do with you and Jeff. Believe me, it'll be like nothing you've ever experienced before.'

'Really?'

Pamela couldn't agree with Casey's casual attitude towards fidelity within marriage, but her words caused a ripple of excitement to pass through her which was far more powerful than her twinges of conscience.

Casey laughed. 'Yeah, really. Do what you feel, baby. Go with it – and forget all this should-I-shouldn't-I? stuff – it's a waste of time.'

'You think so?'

'Honey, I *know* so! And if you're still bothered by that oversized conscience of yours, just think of it as simply another beauty treatment. Therapeutic.'

Casey gave her an exaggerated wink and Pamela laughed, feeling her tension dissipating. It did her good to talk to Casey. Not only had she given her the reassurance that she had sought that Dirk would come to her, she had helped her put the proposed adventure into its proper perspective.

That night as she prepared for bed, Pamela paid special attention to her hair, brushing it until it lay, for once, in a shiny cap, brushing softly against her cheeks. Removing her daytime make-up, she then reapplied a little eyeliner and a soft pink lipstick which gave the merest hint of colour to her face.

Briefly, she toyed with the idea of slipping naked between the fresh silk sheets, deciding at the last minute that she would feel more comfortable in a nightdress. At least she had brought her one strappy, satin affair with her and she drew it slowly over her head, smoothing the pale peach-coloured fabric over her body as she eyed herself critically in the full-length mirror.

Deciding that the bedside lamps were too harsh, she brought in the candleholders from the bathroom and distributed them around the room. Soon, candles were flickering on every available surface, lending the pretty, eau-de-Nil bedroom an almost sultry atmosphere which was exactly in keeping with her mood.

Spraying herself liberally with Chanel No.5, Pamela lay down between the cool sheets, trying to control the butterflies which seemed to be fighting in her stomach.

He came to her as she lay, wakeful, in the gathering dusk, watching the shadows play on the ceiling. She jumped as if the soft knock at the door had been a violent hammering, leaping inelegantly out of bed and having to stop and calm herself before moving over to open the door.

He was carrying two champagne flutes, upside down, between his fingers. In his other hand he had an ice bucket, the neck of a champagne bottle peeking out of the top. Pamela's glance took in the pristine white jacket over crisp black trousers and she raised her eyebrows at the red silk bow-tie.

'I've been to a Rotary dinner,' he whispered, seeing her gaze settle on his neckwear. 'Are you going to let me in?'

Pamela stood aside, putting her hand to her breast as if to still the nervous fluttering of her heart. She had fantasised about this moment all afternoon, imagining over and over how it would be when she opened her bedroom door to find him standing there. Now it was reality and she was gripped by a paralysing shyness which kept her rooted to the spot by the door.

Dirk put the champagne bucket and the two glasses he had dangling from his fingers on to the bedside table, then he turned towards her. Seeing that she had not moved from the door, he went to close it for her, then, summing up her mood in one glance, he picked up her hand and led her to the bed.

'Some champagne, I think,' he said, his voice low.

Pamela sat stiffly on the edge of the bed and watched as he popped the cork – expertly, no noise, no mess – and poured her a generous glassful. Feeling like an unsophisticated girl on her first date, she gulped at the golden liquid, which promptly went down the wrong way.

Dirk slapped her on the back as she coughed and spluttered, offering her a clean white handkerchief to wipe her streaming eyes once she had brought herself back under control.

'Oh dear!' she gasped, handing it back to him, 'what must you think of me?'

She caught his eye and saw the laughter he was trying to hold back and collapsed into fits of giggles. As if her mirth gave him permission to show his own amusement, Dirk laughed with her, leaning his forehead against hers in a brief moment of intimacy.

'What *are* you laughing at?' he asked, his voice teasing.

Pamela shrugged helplessly. 'Just at me – the great seductress!' she giggled helplessly. 'You have to admit; I'm more Ealing studios than Hollywood.'

Dirk chuckled softly. He cupped her face with one hand, his thumb caressing the sensitive hollow behind her ear.

'You know what they say about laughter, don't you?'

Pamela shook her head, smiling still.

'They say that it's one of the most powerful aphrodisiacs.'

Something about the cadence of his voice, rather than his words, made Pamela meet his eyes. The breath caught in her chest as she saw the deep, dark pools of his enlarged pupils and it hit her that he *did* desire her, as a woman, not merely as a client he was required to service. And she realised that it had been bothering her, this suspicion that he might feel *obliged* in some way, bound by his job description to make love to her.

When she spoke, she found that her own voice was hoarse, barely rising above a whisper.

'I thought that sex was supposed to be the most fun you could have *without* laughing?'

Dirk's lips curved upward slightly and his eyes slipped down to caress her mouth.

'Woody Allen doesn't know what he's missing,' he murmured.

'M-maybe he thinks sex is no joking matter?' she stammered.

He had lowered his head so that when he spoke again his breath tickled across her lips.

'Who said anything . . . about jokes?' he said indistinctly.

Pamela could feel the tendrils of desire moving through her limbs as his lips brushed gently over hers, barely touching, yet coaxing her mouth to open involuntarily. Suddenly, it was hard to breathe, the exquisite tension of the moment robbing her of the most basic of human reflexes. Waiting for him to make that final, decisive move towards covering her mouth with his was such sweet torture that Pamela felt she could not bear it.

She could not ever remember wanting to be kissed quite as much as she wanted it now. This man was a stranger to her, though he was fast acquiring as intimate a knowledge of her body as her own husband. She knew nothing about him, not even his last name, and yet, perversely, she felt as if she knew everything about him which was of any importance.

She knew, for example, that his lips were firm, yet soft, his mouth moulded as if by an artist's hand, infinitely kissable. Earlier, she had seen what lay beneath the smartly tailored jacket he still wore and knew that she had liked what she saw. And she knew that he was attracted to her, and that in itself was a powerful spur to the senses, adding an erotic charge to her already fevered imagination.

With a deep sigh, Pamela stopped waiting and claimed his lips herself. They were just as firm and warm as she had known they would be. Her arms came up around his neck as he kissed her with the kind of thoroughness that made her legs grow weak and her stomach melt with longing. God, how she wanted this man!

As she thought it, she marvelled, briefly, at how unshocked she was by her own wantonness. That was her last coherent thought as she followed Casey's heartfelt advice and gave herself over to sensation.

Dirk looked hot as they finally broke away. His

dark eyes spoke unashamedly of his desire as he held her gaze. Swiftly, he pulled off his bow-tie and cast his jacket aside. The buttons of his snowy white shirt strained under his fingers in his haste to unfasten them as he stripped to the waist.

Greedily, Pamela ran her palms over the heated silk of his shoulders, glorying in the finely muscled contours of his arms and chest. Her fingers tangled in the fine mat of black hair which grew in whorls across his pecs and down his midline to the waistband of his trousers. The candlelight played across his tanned skin, casting shadows over his face as she devoured him with her eyes.

He was beautiful to her, from his square jaw and slightly crooked nose above the attractive mouth, to the widely spaced, dark eyes which were looking at her now with such hunger. With a swift flash of perception Pamela realised that it was his desire for her which made him so irresistible to her. She needed this affirmation of her attractiveness after Jeff's betrayal.

Kneeling up on the bed, she pressed herself against him, kissing him deeply and pushing her tongue between his teeth so that she could taste the sweetness of his mouth. She felt hot, consumed by lust as his hands reached up to caress her breasts beneath their thin covering of satin.

He hadn't touched her there before; on the boat he had given her pleasure in as direct a way as possible. Now her nipples crested, pushing eagerly against his palms as he gathered up her breasts.

Breaking away from her lips, he drew one quivering bud into the heated orifice of his mouth. Pamela let her head loll back on her shoulders as he described a circle around it with his tongue, impatient to feel his lips against her bare flesh. But Dirk seemed content to caress her through the satin of her nightdress. As he left one breast and turned his attention to the other, the wet fabric clung coolly to her skin, making the nipple harden to the point of discomfort.

His hands roamed her waist, moving down to feel the shape of her buttocks beneath the long nightdress. As he squeezed and parted her cheeks, Pamela felt the gentle kiss of the cool air against her vulva and realised that she was ready for him already.

Breaking away from her breasts, he looked up at her, his hands coming round her waist so that his thumbs rubbed against her hipbones.

'Take it off,' he whispered.

Pamela needed no further encouragement. Dirk sat back slightly so that he could watch her as she slipped off the bed and stood in front of him. Aware of the erotic intensity of his gaze, she prolonged the moment of tension, revelling in his pleasure. To be desired – nothing could be more arousing.

Slowly, she slipped the shoestring straps of her nightdress first off one shoulder, then the other.

Dirk's eyes followed the movement of her fingers as she caressed the satin-smooth skin of her own arms before pushing the bodice over her breasts. They sprang free, relieved to have the restraint of the cloying, wet fabric removed.

Acting on instinct, Pamela allowed her fingertips to trickle slowly across her chest and over her nipples. Cupping her breasts in her hands, she lifted them, pushing them together so that the deep pink crests pointed yearningly at him. The look which passed across Dirk's face thrilled her. His jaw tightened and a pulse began to beat gently in his temple.

Smiling to herself, she moved her hands down, to her waist, and slowly eased the nightdress over her hips so that it fell in a silky heap around her ankles. She felt a pang, then, of self-consciousness, her self-assurance slipping until she saw the intent expression on Dirk's face.

It was clear that he was holding himself in check, letting her set the pace. Sensing the leashed emotion in him, Pamela revelled in the delicious thrill of anticipation which ran through her. Without realising what she was doing, she flicked her tongue across her lips. Something kicked in her stomach as she realised that Dirk had followed the action with his eyes.

'Wouldn't you be more comfortable out of those trousers?' she asked him hoarsely.

His eyes slipped down to his own lap, where the fabric was stretched so tight by his erection that the seams were under serious strain. Raising his eyes, he smiled at her before standing up. 'Maybe you could help me?'

Pamela moved forward, her hand reaching for the end of his belt. Noting the way his stomach clenched as her fingertips brushed against his skin, Pamela felt an answering tightening in her own belly. Suddenly, she couldn't wait to see him naked, to feel his firm, masculine flesh pressing against the yielding softness of hers, and she dispensed with his belt swiftly before turning her attention to the fastening of his trousers.

Because they were stretched so tight, she struggled to pass the hook through the eye and he had to help her. Underneath, he was wearing black silk boxer shorts which could barely contain his erection. Pushing his trousers down to his ankles, Pamela knelt at his feet and helped him out of his shoes and socks, so that he could step out of his trousers.

His legs were strong and nicely shaped, the tanned skin sparsely furred with black hair. Pamela ran her fingers lightly up the backs of his legs, rising up on her knees so that she was at eye-level with the waistband of his boxers. Looking up at him, she saw that his face was tense. He was watching her, waiting to see what she would do.

Pamela moulded his buttocks through the thin silk of his shorts. They were firm and neat, clenching beneath the probing caress of her hands. Slowly, prolonging the anticipation as long as she could bear it, she ran her fingers lightly beneath the waistband of his boxer shorts until they met at the fastening.

They were both breathing hard as Pamela worked the recalcitrant button through the buttonhole. Easing his shorts down slowly over his hips, as if unwrapping a present, she watched as his cock sprang from the opening, rearing up proudly in front of her eyes.

He was circumcised, the soft, pink head exposed at once to her gaze. Pamela gave in to the urge to touch the velvety skin and he gasped.

'Pamela—'

'Ssh!'

She watched as a drop of thin, clear fluid leaked from the tiny slit, catching it on her tongue and swirling it around his glans. Reaching up, between his legs, she cupped the tight, hairy sacs, absorbing their heat in her palm as she slowly stretched her lips around the tip of his penis. So absorbed was she in what she was doing, she barely noticed that Dirk had reached down and was stroking her hair, urging her to take all of him in her mouth.

She did so, in her own good time, revelling in the feeling of fullness as his cock-head nudged at the back of her throat. She had learned long ago how to relax the muscles of her throat so as not to gag and she was glad of her expertise as she enjoyed him. It was a disappointment when he pulled gently away from her.

Looking up at him quizzically, she saw that a

faint flush had spread across his chest and neck and realised that he had pulled himself back from the brink.

'Stand up,' he said.

Pamela reacted instinctively to the note of command in his voice, rising shakily to her feet and watching him through half closed eyes as he unrolled a condom over his straining penis. He made even that singularly mundane act look erotic, taking his time and caressing himself for her pleasure. Pamela's eyes felt as though she had been deprived of sleep for days, they were so heavy she could barely lift the lids.

Dirk gestured towards the bed.

'Turn around.'

Slowly, Pamela obeyed him. Her arms and legs felt so heavy that to move seemed as difficult as wading through treacle. Behind her now, she sensed that Dirk was also barely controlling himself.

'Strip off the cover.'

There was something about the way he spoke which made her do as he said without hesitation, eager to hear what he would ask of her next. He did not disappoint her.

'Lean over the bed – face down. That's right.'

His voice was low and seductive and Pamela found it hard to breathe.

'Lift your hips . . . feet apart . . . God, you're gorgeous!'

Pamela tried to picture herself as he could see her and failed. Her legs trembled as she waited for his next move, her stomach cramping with excitement.

He reached for her, running his fingertips along her spine so that she shivered.

'You're wet,' he told her, his voice caressing her. At the sound of it she felt a fresh rush of moisture seep from her.

'So wet . . . and warm – I can feel how warm you are without even touching you. Kneel down. Press your breasts against the bed.'

He waited while Pamela obeyed him, then she sensed him kneeling down behind her.

'Will you let me in?' he whispered, close to her ear.

Pamela's throat felt dry and had to force the words up and out through her lips.

'Oh yes!' she whispered, bracing herself against the cool silk sheet.

She felt his lips press against her spine, close to where it ended at the top of the crease between her buttocks. His hands tangled in her hair and then ran along the smooth sweep of her back to rest at her waist. She could feel his penis nudging at the wet, welcoming entrance to her body and she tried to thrust her hips back slightly, but he would not be rushed.

'Slowly,' he whispered. 'I want you to savour every centimetre.'

Pamela gasped as he slipped smoothly into her, edging, as he had promised, centimetre by centimetre so that she was aware of every tiny movement. She could feel the silky walls of her vagina welcome him in, the muscles contracting around him, trying to draw him in faster, deeper.

Dirk's mouth moved across her lower back, his kisses open, wet, mimicking the sucking motion of her sex. As his stomach touched against her bottom and his cock was finally buried in her, he sighed deeply and was still.

Impatient, Pamela wriggled her hips, but he held her immobile, his large hands at her waist, content for the moment merely to rest inside her. Then slowly, with a control that Pamela could not help but admire, he began to move. So slowly she thought she would scream with frustration, he withdrew, then re-entered her, sinking in slightly further this time so that her hips bucked involuntarily against him.

Gradually he built up the tempo, thrusting faster, deeper, so that Pamela's body rocked under the impact. Her breasts slid back and forth over the silk of the sheet, the friction creating a heat which radiated through her whole body. As Dirk's hips worked back and forth, his hands slipped beneath her so that he could feel the greedy swell of her clitoris against his fingers.

His body covered her now, his heat merging with hers, making their bodies stick, then peel apart again. Pamela could not silence the small, rhythmical sounds that came from her throat with every inward thrust. She could feel the building of an orgasm in the concentration of nerve endings at her core and the vocalisation of her excitement grew louder and more urgent.

As her nipples grazed again against the silk and Dirk pistoned in and out of her receptive body, she bore down on his fingers, pushing out her clitoris with desperate need. Sensing what she barely understood she wanted herself, Dirk flicked his fingertip back and forth, beating the little bud lightly until, suddenly, everything seemed to implode and Pamela cried out, 'Oh-oh-oh!'

Her innermost flesh convulsed around Dirk's thrusting penis and his voice joined hers in a triumphal sound which was half shout, half groan as the seed pumped from his body. Pamela felt him sag as his control finally broke and the strength poured from him. Something soared within her at the thought that she had been the one to break that control and she was suffused by a sense of feminine power which made her feel dizzy.

Pressing her hot cheek against the cool sheet, she welcomed the weight of him as he lay across her back, pressing her deeper into the yielding mattress. Then, ever considerate of her, he raised himself up on his elbows and pressed his lips against the centre of her back, sending shivers up her spine.

'Okay?' he whispered.

'Mmmm.'

Pamela closed her eyes and smiled. If only he knew! Her entire body felt limp and she felt a wave of exhaustion break over her.

After a few minutes, she felt Dirk's penis slip

out of her and he stood up. The removal of his body heat made Pamela shiver, and she reluctantly pulled herself up, on to the bed. Too exhausted to move, she merely smiled as Dirk pulled the covers over her.

She listened to his movements as he walked around the room, extinguishing the candles. Gradually, they were enclosed by the soft, velvety darkness, the pungent scent of guttering candles filling the air.

In some ways she wanted nothing more than for Dirk to slip into bed beside her and hold her while she slept, but somehow she knew that he would not. And she knew also that she was glad, because she would not want to wake up beside him in the morning and have to make polite conversation. What had happened tonight was perfect. Exciting, tender, but essentially impersonal. Rather like the therapeutic 'treatment' Casey had suggested she should regard it as.

Before he left, Dirk bent over the bed and brushed her cheek with his lips.

'Good night,' he whispered.

Pamela smiled in the darkness, listening as he padded across the room and closed the door softly behind him. Somehow she thought he understood that she hadn't the energy to reply. And she knew he did not mind.

Chapter Five

PAMELA HAD THE pool to herself the following morning and she made the most of it, ploughing up and down until her arms began to ache. As she rolled over to float on her back, a familiar voice drifted across to her.

'Thank the Lord for that – you made me feel faint, just watching you!'

Opening her eyes, Pamela grinned at Casey. 'Come on in – it's lovely,' she said.

She watched as Casey eased her long, lithe body into the water, wincing slightly at the first shock of the cold.

'It's warm once you're in,' Pamela promised.

Casey began to swim. Strictly a dry-hair swimmer, she executed a leisurely breaststroke the length of the pool until she was level with Pamela.

'So,' she grinned, her straight, white teeth

flashing against the flawless brown of her skin, 'how was it?'

'How do you know he came?' Pamela said coyly.

Casey laughed. 'Because, honey, if you were any more laid-back you'd be horizontal. He came all right – and if your expression is anything to go by, so did you!'

Smiling, Pamela lay back in the water and allowed herself to float.

'Okay, nosy! It was good. It was *very* good. It was very, *very* good – argh!' She gasped as Casey ducked her, spluttering as she came up for air. 'What was that for?'

'Being smug! No more qualms then, about your man?'

Pamela shook her head. She'd thought long and hard about it while she was taking her bath that morning, and she had come to the conclusion that Jeff had broken the rules of their marriage when he had strayed with Dena. Now if there was to be a future for them, they would have to be rewritten, and she was damn sure that she would have a hand in the rewriting!

'No. I'm going to take your advice, Casey, and go with the flow while I'm here. What? What is it?'

Casey seemed to be looking at her strangely, and there was a look in her eyes which made Pamela feel vaguely uncomfortable, and yet, deep down, she felt the unmistakable stirrings of excitement. There was something dangerous in the look that Casey was giving her – something dangerous, and yet compelling.

'You're going to experiment with your sexuality, then?'

'I think so.'

Casey swam alongside her and, unexpectedly, ran one long fingernail gently across Pamela's shoulder. Pamela shivered and she smiled. 'What do you think of the murals?' she asked, out of the blue.

Treading water, Pamela's eyes skittered towards the paintings on the walls.

'They're very ... interesting,' she replied, wondering at the sudden turn the conversation had taken.

Casey smiled at her, her expression cat-like. Her long, straightened hair floated around her head like a skein of black silk on the surface of the water.

'What of the second one?' she asked, her voice no more than a murmur.

Pamela regarded the image of the woman, her thorn-pricked thumb being soothed by the man's tongue while a second woman knelt between her legs, and her skin prickled with awareness. The image of joyous, uninhibited sexuality had made her feel uncomfortable the first time she had seen it – mainly, she knew, because it had aroused her. This response embarrassed her, made her feel confused, and now as she regarded the picture with Casey, those feelings were doubled. She could feel the other woman's eyes on her now and she turned her head slowly to meet her eye.

'Are you bisexual, Casey?'

Pamela wasn't sure what kind of response she expected Casey to give to her direct question, but she certainly had not anticipated that she would throw back her head and laugh.

'Oh Pamela,' she said after a moment, 'you are fond of your labels, honey!'

'I'm sorry,' Pam said, slightly offended by Casey's tone.

'Don't be sorry. You could say that I'm bisexual, I guess. I like girls as well as guys, though strictly in the recreational sense. I like being married. Don't you ever fancy other girls?'

'Of course not!' Pamela replied at once, a little too quickly.

Casey's eyes narrowed and she swam towards her, virtually trapping her against the side of the pool.

'I don't think you're being very honest, Pammie. Don't be scared . . .' She touched a gentle finger against Pamela's tremulous lower lip, her voice dropping an octave as she pressed her lean body against hers under the water. 'Kiss me. Go on – you want to know what it's like, don't you? Kissing another woman?'

Without thinking what she was doing, Pamela nodded her head. Casey was so close, she could feel the barest pressure of her high, firm breasts touching her own, could smell the heavy, feminine scent she always wore and see the glitter of desire deep in her chocolate brown eyes.

'We're friends, you and I – why not try it?'

Pamela held her breath as Casey brushed her lips lightly across hers. They were so soft, so full, totally unlike Dirk's firm lips, or Jeff's masculine mouth. Tentatively, she opened her mouth a little and caught Casey's sweet breath on her tongue. The kiss was so very sensitive and tender, Pam felt herself tremble from head to foot as the other woman's lips moved on hers and the tip of her tongue licked lightly along her inner lip.

'How was that?' Casey whispered, breaking away.

Pamela swallowed hard. 'Nice,' she croaked, aware of a sense of waiting, of holding her breath to see what would happen next.

She was never to know, for at that moment the double doors leading to the pool were opened and two women came bustling through. Casey swam away with her slow, leisurely strokes, leaving Pamela feeling flustered and confused. Watching Casey as she greeted the other women, she marvelled at how cool, how unmoved she seemed, whereas she, she was still trembling, a dull pulse still throbbing expectantly between her thighs.

What had Casey awoken in her? Pamela felt a little thrill of excitement, shot through with fear. Did she really want to find out?

Later, she gave in to a sudden, inexplicable desire to telephone Jeff. His obvious pleasure at hearing her voice was as unexpected as it was gratifying and Pamela felt herself softening towards him a little.

'You must be psychic, Pammie – I was lying awake last night wondering how to get hold of you! Are you all right?'

'I'm fine, Jeff,' she replied, trying to quell the treacherous lurch of her heart at the sound of his voice. How could she feel like this about him still after the pain he'd caused her? Then it registered that he'd said he had wanted to contact her. 'Everything's all right isn't it? Did you want to speak to me for a specific reason?'

'Only . . . I was missing you, darling.'

'Really? Was Dena missing me too?'

Pamela hated herself for the cynical tone to her voice, but could not resist the jibe.

'Dena and I . . . It's over, Pam, for what it's worth. I know that doesn't make what I did right, but it's over now. I promise.'

'I see.'

'Is that all you can say?'

Pamela swallowed at the inconvenient lump of emotion which had risen in her throat. 'What do you want me to say, Jeff?'

There was a momentary pause.

'That you might give me another chance?'

Pamela gripped the receiver, holding on to it as if it was her only friend as she came to terms with the idea that Jeff didn't want to end their marriage, that he was leaving the ultimate decision about their future to her.

'It's too soon, Jeff. I . . . I've been having a few

adventures of my own and—'

'You mean you've been trying to get back at me?'

'I didn't say that—'

'Have you slept with someone else, Pamela?' he demanded, his voice rising.

Pamela heard the anger in his voice, but she also caught the note of underlying panic and she didn't react to the provocation.

'Jeff, I think we should take this as a chance to take a long hard look at what we want from each other and from our relationship.'

'I don't understand, Pamela – can't we just go back to how things were before?'

Pam sighed.

'No, Jeff, I don't think we can. Look, I'll ring you in a day or two and we'll talk some more.'

'Are you sure you can fit me into your busy schedule?' he snapped.

'Don't be like that,' Pamela pleaded, hating the note of bitterness travelling along the telephone wires. 'You owe me a little time. I'll ring you. Bye.' She hung up before he could say another word.

The telephone conversation he had had with Pamela replayed itself over and over in his head as Jeff tried to work that afternoon. There had been something different about her, something . . . more assertive that unnerved him. What had she meant by telling him she was having 'adventures', for Christ's sake?

He closed his eyes and groaned aloud as he

imagined Pamela making love with someone else. Knowing that he himself had probably driven her into another man's arms didn't make it any easier to bear. Supposing she didn't come back?

'You all right, Jeff?' Dena asked as she walked in after her lunch-break.

Jeff took his head out of his hands and looked at her. She had taken to heart his request that she should dress less provocatively and was wearing a demure two-piece skirt-suit in navy blue with a crisp white blouse buttoned to the point just above where her cleavage began. Perversely, she looked even more alluring in her everyday clothes than she had in the more obvious outfits she had worn before.

Something of his thoughts must have shown in his eyes for he noticed Dena's pupils dilate and she half smiled at him.

'Why don't we go to my place for a chat?' she suggested, her voice low and inviting.

Jeff gazed at her, aware that his cock had reacted to her words with predictable enthusiasm. His heart, though, told him that he did not want to go back on his decision to stay faithful to Pamela and he shook his head.

'I think I'll go home. There's nothing happening here that the foreman can't handle.'

He stood up and, aware of Dena's regretful eyes following him, he strode out of the cabin and made for his car.

If Pamela had worried about facing Casey at

77

dinner after their highly charged encounter in the pool, she needn't have. The other girl greeted her enthusiastically as usual and no mention was made of the kiss they had shared. Even so, Pamela was aware of a tension between them, an undercurrent that hadn't been there before.

'I met the most interesting woman this lunchtime – I must introduce you. See – over there.'

Pamela followed the line of her nod and saw a strikingly handsome woman sitting with an equally attractive man at a table set for two across the room. The woman had the kind of sharp, well-groomed looks which made it hard to guess her age. Her hair, so black it had to have been colour-treated, was cut in a severe bob, the ends of which followed her jawline, tapering to a sharp vee. Her features seemed over-large in her small, heart-shaped face. The widely spaced, almond-shaped eyes were outlined heavily with black kohl and her full lips were painted a bright, uncompromising red.

Her companion looked vaguely familiar and Pamela frowned as she tried to recall where she had seen him before. He had the looks of an ageing matinée idol. Probably somewhere in his early fifties, he had a craggy, well-used face, the skin tanned as only the very rich can afford to tan. Even from this distance Pamela could see that his eyes were a bright, twinkling blue and she smiled involuntarily as, perhaps sensing her appraising gaze, he turned them on her. The smile that turned up the corners of his mouth was delightful, reinforcing Pamela's first impression that she had seen him before.

'Gorgeous, isn't he?' Casey purred in her ear, making Pamela start guiltily.

'I bet he was a heart-breaker when he was young,' she muttered non-committally.

Casey chuckled softly. 'He looks to me like the kind of guy who improves with age. His name is Andrew Slattery.'

She waited for the recognition to dawn on Pamela's features and was not disappointed. '*Drew* Slattery – the actor?'

'You got it, hon,' Casey said, pleased to be able to be the one to impart the information. 'Though he hasn't made many films lately. Apparently Alice vets all his scripts and nothing has come up to scratch for years now.'

'Alice is the woman with him, I take it?'

'Yeah. Manager and wife. I said we'd meet them for a drink in the drawing-room after dinner, if that's okay with you?'

Pamela nodded, excited to be sitting in the same room as Drew Slattery, never mind at the prospect of meeting him. As she ate, she recalled the times as a teenager when she had sat in a darkened cinema watching Drew Slattery's films, imagining that the arm creeping around her shoulders was his rather than whatever spotty youth was her current escort. On screen he had simmered with a subtle, mature sexuality which Pamela had recognised, perhaps at a subconscious level at that age, that had never failed to arouse her.

And now, here he was, the object of her every pubescent fantasy, eating across from her. And later she would actually meet him, on equal terms.

Glancing around the dining-room, Pamela was surprised to note that no one else appeared to be paying the actor any attention. As Casey had said, it had been years since he'd made a film, but surely she wasn't the only one who remembered him?

At last, dinner was over and the guests wandered off to their various destinations. Pamela followed Casey into the powder room where she touched up her lipstick and combed her hair before surveying her reflection critically in the full-length mirror. Dinner was the only part of the day when the guests changed out of their comfortable towelling robes and most made up for their daytime sloth by really going to town.

This evening, Pamela was wearing a plain, powder-blue dress with shoestring straps which criss-crossed at the back. Though unpretentious in design, the light jersey fabric of the dress followed the lines of her body so closely that it was impossible to wear underwear underneath it. Consequently, Pamela had been feeling vaguely sexy all evening and she was both apprehensive and excited at the thought of her meeting with Drew Slattery. Apprehensive because she had never met anyone famous before and was afraid she might act like a star-struck idiot, and excited because there was always the possibility that Drew might find her attractive. Pamela bit her lip at the thought. Did she really want to turn him on by flaunting her lack of underwear?

He and his wife, Alice, turned as Casey and Pamela entered the drawing-room. A quick glance around told Pamela that there was no one else in the discreet bar area, and this gave her the feeling of walking into the drawing-room of someone's house.

Alice stepped forward to greet Casey at once while Pamela's eyes caught and held Drew's. When they had walked in, he had been leaning against the bar, sipping from a champagne flute. In his silver-grey lounge suit and pale blue shirt he had looked the epitome of an English gentleman. But as he straightened and greeted Pamela his cultured but unmistakably American accent gave the lie to his appearance.

'I'm Drew Slattery,' he told her, holding out his hand, 'and you must be Pamela?'

Pam nodded, conscious of the dry warmth of his palm against hers. 'It's a lovely surprise to find you here,' she told him, her voice unnaturally high, 'I saw all your films when I was young.'

She cursed herself inwardly for her ridiculous *faux pas*, but Drew merely tipped back his head and laughed. It was a deep, velvety sound which sent shivers across Pamela's skin. She had not dared to hope he would be as compellingly attractive in real life as he was on the screen.

'I'm surprised you recognise me – I wasn't so grey in my film-making days,' he said ruefully, making Pamela aware for the first time that his still thick, dark hair was shot through with silver.

If anything this sign of maturity made him even more attractive in her eyes and she smiled.

'I didn't mean to imply that you were old – merely experienced,' she said, realising at once that she had again said something that could be taken to have a double meaning. Flustered – she wasn't normally this inept – she continued, 'Are your film-making days, as you call them, over completely now?'

Drew smiled, his eyes moving to Alice, who was deep in conversation with Casey, before he answered.

'Probably. Life has a habit of moving on, wouldn't you agree? Would you like some champagne?'

Pamela followed him to the bar, watching his hands as he poured her a drink. They were slim and long-fingered, the skin tanned and lined, beginning to show his age.

'*Santé*,' he murmured, raising his glass to hers and holding her eye as he drank.

God, but he was attractive, Pamela mused as she felt herself swimming in the clear blue depths of his eyes. She could barely believe that here she was, staring into the eyes of the film star she had adored for years! Better still, he seemed not to be averse to her company. Steady, she warned herself, remembering belatedly that his wife was

82

standing by the French doors with Casey, mere feet away – this was only a carefully polished charm which he would have developed over the years. No need to take it personally!

At that moment, Casey came over to join them, bringing Alice with her. 'Pamela – this is Alice Slattery. Alice – my friend Pamela.'

'How do you do?' Alice Slattery asked coolly.

'How do you do?' Pamela took the elegantly manicured fingertips which were offered and suffered the other woman's unsmiling scrutiny. She wasn't sure what Alice was looking for, all she knew was that she felt fearfully uncomfortable under the other woman's gimlet eye. Then Alice smiled, a wide, generous smile which completely transformed her rather harsh-looking features.

'It's such a pleasure to meet new people, wouldn't you agree? Casey and I go back a long way.'

Pamela glanced at Casey in surprise. She hadn't mentioned that she knew the Slatterys.

'I can see you've captivated my husband – he always has an eye for a pretty face, don't you, darling?'

Pamela glanced uncomfortably at Drew, but he smiled easily at his wife.

'And thank God for that!' he replied.

To Pamela's relief, the older woman laughed and the slight tension which seemed to have been building between them all was shattered.

'I commend your taste, my dear,' Alice told

him, unexpectedly reaching over to cup Pamela's chin. With a grip which was gentle, though strangely compelling, she turned Pamela's face from side to side, examining it. 'She is rather lovely, isn't she, in an unconventional way?'

'You know I prefer women with less obvious charms,' Drew murmured, his eyes on his wife's. 'They tend to be more interesting.'

'Absolutely, my love.'

Pamela, disconcerted by this exchange between them, conducted as if she wasn't there, moved back slightly to dislodge Alice's hand. Alice turned then, scrutinising her narrowly before the smile transformed her features again.

'Don't mind us, Pamela dear – we're perfectly harmless!'

Pamela blinked uncertainly, turning gratefully to Casey as she took her by the elbow.

'Why don't we all sit down?' Casey suggested, steering Pamela over to the sofa by the French doors.

The next hour or so passed pleasantly enough. The Slatterys ordered more champagne and the conversation flowed as freely as the wine. Casey and Alice appeared to have a great many friends in common and they chatted together, leaving Pamela and Drew rather in each other's company. Pamela could not help but be secretly flattered that Drew seemed to be paying her special attention, and once she realised that Alice did not appear to mind his outrageous flirting, she relaxed and began to enjoy herself. After all, there was no harm in it.

When Drew rose and suggested that they take a walk in the gardens, Alice smiled up at him and waved an indulgent hand.

'You go with Pamela, darling – Casey and I have so much gossip to catch up on! You must think us very rude, Pamela – I am sorry if we've been excluding you.'

'Not at all,' Pam replied hastily. 'Drew has been telling me about his last film.'

The other woman smiled knowingly. 'I thought he would take care of you!' she said, again making Pamela aware of an undercurrent between husband and wife which she didn't quite understand. 'Enjoy your walk.'

Pamela followed Drew through the French doors and down the wide stone steps to the patio. Something in Alice's tone had made her feel uneasy, but she dismissed the feeling as fanciful. After all, there was no harm in strolling with Drew in the gardens of the Hall, was there?

She wasn't quite so sure of this when, once they were out of sight of the main building, Drew took her hand in his.

'I love these light evenings, don't you?' he said as they strolled through the rose garden. The scent of the flowers still hung on the quiet air even though the grass was beginning to dew beneath their feet.

'This is my favourite time of day,' she told him, 'especially in the summer when the warmth lingers, as if the day is reluctant to give way to the night.'

Drew stopped walking so that Pamela found herself turning to face him. Her breath caught in her throat as she saw the way his blue eyes had darkened as he looked at her. Suddenly she was very aware of his nearness in the fragrant rose garden and of their isolation from the Hall.

'How very poetic,' he murmured, moving very slightly towards her.

Pamela knew that he was about to kiss her, knew and felt that she should take some evasive action. After all, he was married, and his wife was close by, but something rooted her to the spot. His physical magnetism, her own curiosity – the reasons seemed superfluous at that moment as his mouth descended to hers.

His lower lip was slightly larger than the upper one, and soft, so that Pamela's first reaction was one of disappointment. Her second was to press her own mouth harder on to his to deepen the kiss. A shiver went through him as she took the initiative and wound her arms about his neck and she felt an answering thrill echo deep in her belly. Drew's hands stroked up and down her back, moving the thin fabric of her dress over her naked skin.

After a moment, he drew away. 'What would you say if I asked you to come up to my room later?' he asked, his voice shaky.

Pamela's eyebrows rose. 'I would say, "what about your wife?",' she told him primly.

To her surprise, Drew smiled. That smile had had the power to cause millions of women around the world to tremble with suppressed desire, and to have it focused entirely on herself made Pamela feel weak. She closed her eyes as he kissed her again.

'Alice and I have an . . . understanding,' he told her after a few minutes. 'Believe me, she would not mind. On the contrary.'

Pamela gazed up at him, intrigued. On the one hand she was undeniably turned on by who he was. Kissing him was like the fulfilment of a long-held fantasy. On the other, there had been something curiously asexual about the kiss. Certainly it had failed to set light to the slow burning embers of her desire.

'I don't know, Drew,' she said, intending to let him down gently.

'Please,' he said, forestalling her refusal. 'We could have some fun. I think you'd enjoy it.'

'You don't know me,' she protested mildly, puzzled by his choice of words.

Drew smiled and brushed the backs of his fingers gently across the tips of her breasts. Pamela looked down, and they both watched as her nipples hardened beneath their flimsy covering. Embarrassed by her immediate response, she made to cover them with her hands, but Drew caught them, entwining her fingers with his.

'Don't,' he whispered, his voice low and slightly husky. He smiled, a slight cynicism edging his voice as he spoke again. 'I'm rarely wrong about people.'

Pamela looked into his eyes and was struck once again by a little shiver of curiosity. She had the strangest, most insistent feeling that he was right: she *would* enjoy meeting him later. She also had an instinct, equally strong, that he had the capacity to surprise her. Impulsively, she smiled at him.

'All right,' she said.

A look of intense excitement passed across Drew's handsome features.

'Good,' he said, tucking one of her hands in the crook of his arm and turning her back towards the Hall. 'Let's re-join the others, shall we?'

Pamela was surprised at his sudden desire to go back inside, but she walked alongside him without comment. Perhaps she had been rash to agree to go to his room later, but that didn't really bother her too much. She could always phone him from her room and tell him she had changed her mind.

Casey was in the process of pouring coffee when they arrived and Alice set out two more cups for them. Sitting close beside Pamela on one of the sofas, Drew frequently touched her knee, or patted her hand, as if to reassure himself that she was still there. Feeling Alice's eyes on one such caress, Pamela edged away from him slightly, as if to dissociate herself from his actions. When she looked up, she caught Alice's eye and was disconcerted to see that the other woman was smiling.

After a few minutes, Alice pronounced that it

was time for her and Drew to retire.

'Come along, Andrew,' she said, addressing him as she might a ten-year-old child, 'it's been a long day. Say good night to Pamela.'

Drew leaned across to Pamela and kissed her chastely on the cheek. 'You will come, won't you?' he whispered urgently in her ear, 'you won't forget?'

'Andrew!'

He jumped visibly as Alice spoke sharply to him from the door, then he stood up. Pamela was surprised by the almost feverish glint in his eye as he turned to her and said good night.

After a few moments, Pamela became aware that Casey was watching her watching Drew's exit.

'Sexy devil, isn't he?'

Pamela frowned and poured herself another cup of coffee.

'I don't know. I thought so, but there's something . . . missing.'

'Something missing?' Casey echoed, her tone vaguely teasing.

'Yes. Oh, I don't know what it is!'

Casey laughed at her frustration. 'Did he ask you up to his room?'

Pamela looked at her in surprise. 'Yes, he did.'

'Me too.'

'What? Drew invited you to his room?' Pamela was incredulous.

'No, honey. Alice did.'

Casey was silent for a few moments, waiting for

what she had said to sink in. Pamela frowned, uncomfortably aware that there had been an undercurrent to the evening that was beyond her experience.

'I see,' she said shortly, not sure whether she wanted to fully understand.

As if sensing her apprehension, Casey leaned forward and squeezed her hand.

'You will do, Pammie, if you come up with me. Don't look so worried, hon – it's all part of going with the flow!'

Pamela smiled weakly, aware that her eyes were overbright and her stomach was fluttering with nerves. Was she ready for some kind of an orgy? And how would it work, with three women and only one man? The memory of Casey's lips on hers earlier at the pool made her tremble. Is that what she wanted?

Catching Casey's dark, calm gaze, Pamela smiled slowly.

'All right,' she agreed.

Casey flashed her straight, impossibly white teeth at her in a grin that was pure mischief.

'Let's have another coffee, shall we? We don't want them to think we're *too* eager!'

Pamela's second cup tasted like sawdust as she sipped at it. She could not shake off the sense that she was about to commit herself to something momentous, something that she would never be able to forget. Watching Casey pick up her cup, she admired the long, elegant fingers, adorned as always by the scarlet-painted nails. A sudden recollection of the violent splashes of red she had noticed in the murals at the swimming pool came into her mind and she felt a deep, low pulse begin to throb between her legs. The thought of Casey's fingers roaming over her own body intensified the pulse and Pamela wriggled slightly on her seat.

'Let's go,' Casey said, her voice low.

As Pamela followed Casey up the stairs to the Slatterys' bedroom she was aware that her muscles were tense, as if ready to turn and run. Yet she knew that she would not run, her curiosity had been too thoroughly roused.

Pausing outside the bedroom door, Casey glanced at Pamela. Seeing that she was not about to back out, she knocked, twice. Alice's resonant, authoritative voice rang out. 'It's open.'

Opening the door, Casey stood aside to let Pamela enter first. Pinning a bright smile on her face, she walked in – and stopped in her tracks.

'Oh my God!' she breathed, her hand flying to her chest.

Whatever she had expected, it hadn't been this. Alice was dressed from top to toe in shiny black PVC, complete with plumed helmet and four-inch high ankle boots. But Pamela barely glanced at her – it was Drew who held her attention.

He had his back to her, his face pressed into one of the support posts of the elaborate four-poster bed. An intricate pattern of leather thongs interspersed with silver links criss-crossed his broad back and his arms were stretched high above his head, bound to the top of the post. A strange metal contraption, like a rigid bar, was attached at either end to his ankles, forcing them apart so that his legs were held open and the shadowy cleft between his buttocks was revealed.

Pamela's eyes were drawn like a magnet to the vulnerable white skin of his bottom, her stomach tightening with a curious, shameful mixture of horror and excitement as she saw that it was patterned by some half a dozen pink stripes, apparently freshly caused by the thin cane which was now leaning, with symbolic artistry, against the side of his leg.

Chapter Six

THE TENSION IN the room was palpable as everyone waited for Pamela to react. In the end, it was Casey who broke the loaded silence.

'Oh Alice,' she said, a streak of amusement running through her voice, 'trust you to go and start without us!'

Alice raised one ironic eyebrow and nodded towards Pamela. 'I thought that dear Pamela might appreciate my warming him up a little for her,' she said lightly, bringing Pam's attention back to her.

Pamela merely stared at the other woman, realising for the first time that she was naked beneath the PVC basque, the thick, black fur which covered her mons exposed at the apex of her thighs. The smell of arousal, both male and female, was thick in the air. It made Pamela feel dizzy, disoriented and she cast her gaze wildly around until she found Casey, not knowing what to do.

'Your little friend seems shocked, Casey,' Alice purred.

Pamela felt herself bristle at the insultingly derisive tone in the older woman's voice and she squared her shoulders.

'I'm more surprised than shocked, Alice,' she pronounced, amazed at how light and calm her voice sounded. 'Does that disappoint you?'

She smiled to herself as she recognised the flash of frustration which passed across Alice's features and she realised that she had inadvertently hit upon the truth. For whatever reason, Alice Slattery had hoped to catch her off-guard. Rising to the challenge, Pamela vowed that there was no way that she was going to let the other woman see that she had succeeded.

Mustering a self-assurance she was far from feeling, she strolled over to where Drew was waiting. Running her palm over his shoulders, she noticed how he trembled under her touch.

'Are you enjoying this, Drew?' she asked him softly.

He sighed, so deeply that it sounded as though it had travelled up from his toes. That was answer enough for Pamela and she stepped back, glancing uncertainly at Casey. To her relief, the other girl came to her aid.

'Untie him, Alice – it's no fun if we can't see his face! Pammie and I will watch for now.'

Relieved that she was not going to be expected actively to participate in a tableau which, to her, seemed extremely weird, Pamela went over to the long couch and sat beside Casey. Casey immediately pressed her lips against the side of Pamela's hair, drawing her closer to her with one arm about her shoulders.

'I'm not sure about this,' Pam whispered in her ear.

'Just watch,' Casey murmured, giving her shoulder a reassuring squeeze. 'It'll be all right.'

Alice was unfastening Drew's bonds now. As he turned, Pamela half expected to see that he was erect. She was shocked to see that his penis had been bound in a tight sheath of black leather. This had been strapped against his left thigh, so that he could not become erect even if he wanted to.

This was interesting enough, but more intriguing still was the expression on his face. There was shame, certainly, in the glance he shot her from beneath his lashes, but his debasement was coloured by an irrepressible gleefulness. It left Pamela in no doubt that he was enjoying himself.

She could almost feel his tension as he sensed Alice moving up behind him. A shudder went through him, making him close his eyes in a precursor to ecstasy. Alice's arms came about his shoulders and she pressed her partially clad body against his back. In one hand she held the thick, stubby handle of a black leather whip, its numerous fronds dangling down before his eyes.

'Your little friend is worried about this, Andrew,' she cooed, her scarlet-painted lips leaving a smear across his cheek. 'She might want me to spare you.'

A look of horrified panic chased across Drew's features and he looked at Pamela pleadingly. Pam raised her eyebrows slightly, instinctively aware that this was a show being staged by Alice for her benefit, and that she was not required to participate in any way other than passively – at least for now.

'*I* think you should be punished – I think you have behaved very badly – what do you think, Andrew?'

'I agree with you, my love,' he whispered, his voice cracking as if his throat had run dry.

Alice smiled and, sticking out her tongue, she swirled it around the whorls of his ear, making him shudder.

'You know you shouldn't have gone lusting after Pamela, darling, don't you?'

Drew nodded, closing his eyes briefly. When he opened them again, Pamela saw that they were feverishly bright. He was looking in her direction, but she guessed he was not seeing her at all, caught up as he was in viewing his own, inner landscape.

'Once again you've let your brain slip into your cock.'

Alice sighed theatrically, and moved away from him, standing so that he could just see her from the corner of his eye. Drew could not take his eyes off her fingers which toyed idly with the leather fronds at the end of the whip.

'He's always been the same, you see,' she said, half to herself, casting a quick, rueful smile at

Pamela and Casey. 'He was a good actor – but he could have been a great one if it wasn't for *that*!' She flicked the whip dismissively against his leather-covered crotch and turned away in mock disgust.

'It's true!' Drew suddenly cried out, his eyes following Alice slavishly as she paced across the room in her high heeled boots. 'I can't control myself . . .'

Alice shook her head in mock sorrow.

'You know what I'm going to have to do now, don't you, Andrew?' she said, her tone almost conversational.

He dropped his eyes as if in shame and, after a moment, he nodded.

Alice shook her head, every inch the exasperated mistress.

'Very well. Release your penis,' she commanded wearily.

Pamela's eyes widened as she watched Drew, the movie star of her dreams, fumble with the leather fastenings to his bondage. The sense of unreality which had enfolded her as she walked into the room persisted, and yet she could sense a subtle shift in her own reaction to the scene being acted out before her. Her initial response to seeing Drew bound and exposed had been one of horror, tinged a little with embarrassment.

Now, watching his hands as he unlaced himself, she found herself affected by his obvious excitement and, to her surprise, she felt the first flutter of arousal deep in the pit of her stomach.

As if sensing Pamela's tension, Casey curled her long fingers over one of her hands and squeezed it gently. Pamela did not move away, she merely left her hands resting in her lap, trying not to think of how close the other girl's fingers were to the slowly awakening centre of her.

As soon as it was released from the cruel restraint, Drew's long, slender cock sprang erect, standing out from his body. Apparently dismayed, he clasped his hands over it and raised anguished eyes to Alice.

'I'm sorry, my love,' he whispered.

There was a cruel twist to Alice's smile as she advanced upon him. With a sharp flick of her wrist, she wrapped the whip around his forearms, making him move his hands away.

To Pamela's amazement, he was, if anything, harder still, in spite of the threat of the sinister black leather whip close by. Or perhaps *because* of it? Pamela marvelled that she still had so much to learn about the male sexual response.

'Dear, dear me – you don't look very contrite, Andrew! Does he, Pamela?'

At the sound of her name, Pam's attention was jerked back to the tableau before her and she shook her head. 'Um . . . no . . .'

Alice turned back to Drew, who was gazing at her almost worshipfully.

'This is worse than I thought.' She lifted the whip and blew on the fronds thoughtfully. 'Fetch the lubricant, Andrew.'

Her words produced the most extraordinary

effect on Drew. Before Pamela's astonished eyes, he fell to his knees and wrapped his arms around Alice's legs. Burying his face in her naked crotch, he began to beg.

'No! Not that! Please, please . . .' he cried, his voice muffled by her flesh.

He jerked as Alice brought the whip down across his back. Pamela winced, sure the blow must have hurt him, but as he turned away, she saw that it had hardly marked his back, merely turning the skin a light rose pink.

'Don't dawdle – we've all got better things to do with our time than waste it on you!'

Drew opened a drawer and returned with a large tube of lubricating jelly which he held out to Alice. She made no move to take it from him, merely tutting with exasperation and tapping the whip against her boots.

'You know what to do,' she snapped.

Drew's face was a picture of unalloyed misery as he unscrewed the cap of the lubricant.

'Hurry up!'

He fumbled with the tube as Alice snapped at him again, squeezing a generous amount of lubricant in the palm of one hand before looking at her expectantly.

'On your knees!'

Drew shook his head, and for a moment, Pamela thought he was going to refuse. She held her breath, letting it out on a long sigh as he slowly sank to his knees before them.

He had a beautiful body, tanned and firm, the

skin still elastic despite his age. As he leaned forward on to his elbows, Pamela admired the play of his muscles beneath his skin.

'Turn around!' Alice barked, flicking his buttocks with her whip. 'Do you think it's your face we want to see?'

A dark flush of colour tinged Drew's cheeks as he obeyed, moving on his elbows and knees so that the three women were presented with an unimpeded view of his upturned rump. Pamela glanced at Casey uncertainly. The other girl grinned at her, a spark of mischief twinkling in her velvety brown eyes. She winked at Pamela before turning her eyes back to the man grovelling at their feet. The soft pad of her thumb passed across the back of the hand she was still holding, and Pamela shivered.

Becoming impatient with the slowness of Drew's actions, Alice brought the whip down across his buttocks, striping them pale pink.

'Get on with it!' she said as he gasped aloud.

Pamela watched in disbelief and with a certain amount of anticipation. That the highly charged atmosphere in the room had affected her in such a way bothered her – but not enough so that she wanted to leave.

Slowly, as if he was relishing his centre-stage role and wanted to make it last, Drew reached behind himself and grasped his buttocks. With one hand he separated the taut globes, while with the other he lathered his crease with the lubricant, working it into the small, pink hole of his anus.

100

Pamela could only guess at the purpose of this display. What was patently obvious, though, was that Drew himself was powerfully aroused by exhibiting himself in this way. A fine dew of sweat shone on his immaculately tanned skin and his breathing was audible in the silent bedroom.

Alice walked over to him and stroked one trembling buttock almost lovingly before turning to Casey and Pamela.

'Well, my dears – which of you would like the pleasure of punishing him for his lasciviousness?'

Pamela's heart seemed to skip a beat and her eyebrows rose in alarm. She might be finding this scene titillating, but she was quite sure that she did not want to take the enormous step from observer to participant!

Luckily, Casey seemed to have no such reservations. With a broad grin, she uncurled her long body from the chaise and sauntered over to Alice. Taking the whip from her, she tested it against her own thigh before studying her target. Then, with a broad wink at Pamela, she raised her arm.

Drew cried out as the lash kissed one raised buttock. It was a curious sound, a mixture of pain and pleasure that Pamela had never heard before. It seemed to echo round the room, sending strange signals up and down her spine.

Casey waited while Drew brought himself back under control before repeating the manoeuvre, this time on the other buttock. Pamela felt hot. Drew's excitement was like a living thing in the room, a fifth presence, affecting all of them. Alice, who had taken Casey's place at Pamela's side, leaned into her, brushing her lips briefly across Pamela's temple. Pamela jumped as if she had been scalded, and she heard Alice chuckle softly.

As she watched Casey apply the whip to Drew's naked rear, she gradually became aware that Alice had placed her hand on her thigh and was massaging her leg through the thin jersey fabric of her dress. Though her initial instinct was to move away, Pamela was aware that the sensation wasn't an unpleasant one. She could smell the other woman's perfume, mingling with the more intimate aroma emanating from her uncovered pubis which more than hinted at her arousal.

By the time Casey had tired of whipping Drew, Pamela was finding it strangely difficult to breathe. Alice's hand was resting on her lower belly now, the fingertips stroking downward to the apex of her thighs. She removed her hand reluctantly as Casey passed the whip back to her.

'Had enough, Casey?' Alice drawled.

Casey smiled.

'This is your show, honey. I don't want to take all the limelight!'

Alice laughed, leaping to her feet and unexpectedly giving Casey a smacking kiss, full on the lips. Casey's hands came out to steady her and the two women stared at each other. Pamela watched, mesmerised, recognising the swift flare of desire which had reared up between them.

They were all distracted by Drew's faint moan of protest at being neglected.

'Raise your hips, Andrew darling – I have something for you,' Alice purred, walking over to the chest of drawers in the corner and fetching something from one of the drawers.

Drew obeyed her eagerly, pushing his bottom, darkened now to a deep, rosy pink, into the air.

'Open up,' Alice said matter-of-factly, brandishing a small, flesh-coloured dildo.

Pamela's breath hurt in her chest as she watched Alice grease the miniature phallus with the lubricating fluid and run it teasingly up and down Drew's spine. By the time she trailed it along the glistening crease between his buttocks, he was frantic with desire, waggling his hips from side to side like a cat on heat.

'My my, aren't we eager,' Alice said mockingly as she pressed the object against his sphincter.

Pamela could not take her eyes from the small circle of muscle as it first resisted the intrusion, then seemed to pout to welcome it as Alice eased the dildo home. Once it was fully inside him, she strapped the thin loop of flesh-coloured elastic around his waist, presumably so that it could not become lost inside him.

Drew was breathing heavily and as he turned slightly to one side, Pamela could see that his cock was straining fit to burst. Alice reached beneath him and gave his shaft a swift, almost friendly squeeze before turning to Pamela.

'Well, darling – you are the injured party in all

this. What would you like to use? The whip? The cane? Or the crop, perhaps?'

Pamela stared at Alice, her tongue pressing through lips which had grown suddenly dry. She was gripped by a sudden, shocking need to take Alice up on her offer, to see what it felt like to really dominate a man sexually. There was something appallingly erotic about the sight of Drew, crouched on all fours. His poor, abused behind was flaming, the tendons in his neck straining as he sought to maintain his position, the absurd mock phallus embedded deep in his body while his rigid cock strained, all but forgotten by the women, between his legs. How did he feel, displaying himself in this way, reduced to nothing more than an object for their amusement?

How would Jeff feel in such a position? The thought of her husband pushed into Pamela's consciousness without her permission, but it failed to distract her from the matter in hand. Rather, the idea of Jeff thus subjugated gal-vanised her into action and she heard her own voice, firm and decisive, say, 'I'll use the crop.'

Alice's eyebrows rose and Pamela exalted in the look of grudging respect which crept into the other woman's eyes. Clearly, she had expected Pamela to refuse the challenge. Casey passed Pamela the thin, whippy riding crop with an encouraging grin.

'You'll find the inside of his thighs quite responsive,' she said helpfully.

Drew trembled visibly as he realised that some-one new was about to whip him. Alice stood back to give Pamela room. Pam looked down at the shivering male form and thought of Jeff with Dena. Setting her jaw, she raised her arm and brought the crop down across the top of his buttocks.

The crop made a satisfying whistling sound as it cut through the air and the small leather loop at the end slapped against his bare flesh. Drew's cock twitched and he let the air out through his teeth in a low whistle. Taking Casey's advice, Pamela turned her attention to the vulnerable flesh on the inside of his upper thighs and within minutes the white flesh was glowing pinkly.

Pamela paused for breath. She hadn't realised that it would be such hard work! Perspiration beaded her upper lip and her underarms felt damp as she breathed heavily. There was a discreet pop of a cork across the room and Casey passed her a bubbling glass of champagne. Pamela gulped gratefully at it before turning back to Drew.

He was shaking, his knees spread wide apart, the dildo poking obscenely from his anus as he waited to see what she would do next. Pamela stroked the supple end of the riding crop along the seam of his testes, provoking an involuntary shudder from him which made her smile. She felt horribly powerful – cruel, even – with him at her mercy like this.

Alice and Casey were silent, watching her as she repeated the action. Drew's balls were tight and full, the hair-roughened skin stretched tight. With a streak of malevolence Pamela had never dreamed she possessed, she flicked the little leather loop against the bulging sacs.

He came at once, violent spurts of semen spattering the carpet as he cried out in anguish. The three women watched him as he thrust his hips back and forth, as if simulating intercourse, and the seed poured from his body in jagged bursts.

Suddenly, Pamela felt disgusted with herself and what she had done. She dropped the crop and backed away, confused by the strength of her reaction. She didn't know what had made her feelings change – until the moment of Drew's climax she had been enjoying inflicting this clearly welcome humiliation on him. Substituting Jeff for Drew in her imagination had made it easy.

Then it came to her with a flash of insight. That was it – she didn't want to hurt Jeff. The very idea was abhorrent to her. Though he had caused her untold pain, she loved him and inflicting pain on him in return, albeit a very different kind, was not the answer.

'Hey, baby – sit down. Have some more champagne.' Casey's arms came about her and Pamela allowed her friend to lead her back to the chaise. She sank on to it gratefully and drank deeply from her glass. She might be disgusted by her behaviour, but she could not deny that she was powerfully aroused by it. The tender membranes between her legs felt swollen and moist and her clitoris beat with a steady pulse.

Casey was stroking her hair, soothing her as Alice went round to Drew's head. He raised it and looked at her.

'You weren't supposed to come, Andrew,' she drawled derisively. 'Now you're going to have to pay a forfeit. Now – let me see . . .' Her eyes flickered over Pamela and Casey. 'I think that Pamela deserves some reward for her good work, don't you?'

Pam's head shot up in alarm and she shook her head. Alice smiled.

'No? I don't blame you, Pam, darling – he's not a very pretty sight, is he? Hardly worthy to give you pleasure. But he wants to serve you – don't you, Andrew?'

Drew gazed up adoringly at his wife and nodded.

'You see? I know – we'll blindfold him. That way he can make you come without enjoying looking at you. Would you like that, Pamela?'

Pam wanted to say no, to walk away, but the throb between her thighs was growing stronger, demanding to be satisfied. She did not resist when Casey helped her hitch her skirt up to her waist as Alice tied a blue silk scarf tightly around Drew's head.

He crawled towards her eagerly, his hot breath brushing across her stockinged legs as he reached her. Across the room, Alice and Casey climbed on to the bed and faced each other, just as Drew began to kiss and caress the tops of Pamela's feet.

Pamela watched them as they helped each other undress. Casey's body was as magnificent as she had imagined it would be. Her high breasts stood proud above a long, slender torso which was almost boyish with no lavish curves, but with a lean, though thoroughly feminine beauty which made Pamela catch her breath.

Alice's skin was very white against the flawless ebony of Casey's body, and curvaceous in comparison. As she bent her head to take one of Casey's nipples in her mouth, Pamela felt a dart of what she could only describe as jealousy. She gasped as she realised that she wished it was her tasting the tight, taut flesh, that it was *her* tongue flicking against the crest.

Drew had reached the soft flesh of her inner thighs now, but she was virtually oblivious to him, too caught up with her fantasy about Casey. She watched the two women caressing each other as Drew's lips sought and found the heated folds of her vulva.

Without really realising what she was doing, Pamela allowed her legs to fall apart, giving him freer access to her body. His lips were tentative as he gently nipped and licked his way along the slippery channels of her most intimate flesh.

Pamela could not tear her eyes away from the two women. Casey was pressing her small breasts with their tight, purplish areolae against the lush, strawberry-tipped crests of Alice's nipples.

Pamela imagined how it must feel to have another woman's softness pressed against her own, to feel feminine, yielding flesh beneath her fingers instead of hard muscles. The very idea caused a fresh rush of moisture to seep between her sex-lips.

Drew had located her clitoris now and he began to lathe it with his tongue, his strokes becoming more sure, more confident as she thrust her pelvis forward. To Pamela he had become nothing more than a means by which she could assuage the mounting, burning need building in her as she watched Casey masturbating Alice. Casey's long fingers moved in and out of the other woman's nest of dark hair in an almost leisurely way, her thumb caressing the bone which sat just above her clitoris. Pamela could see the dew from Alice's body glistening on Casey's dark skin and her breath began to hurt in her chest.

How must it feel? Surely another woman would know exactly the right amount of pressure to apply, would sense the appropriate rhythm and speed . . .

Alice was gasping, her fingers digging into Casey's shoulders as she raced towards her climax. Pamela's eyes grew wide as she watched the other woman throw her legs apart and buck her hips to meet Casey's fingers.

'Yes – oh God – yes, yes yes!' she almost screamed as she tipped over the edge into orgasm.

Seconds later, Pamela felt her own clitoris throb and everything seemed to fragment around her. She slumped, exhausted, against the back of the chaise, pressing the heel of her hand down on to her mound to prolong the sensation after Drew took his mouth away.

When she opened her eyes, she saw that Drew had torn off his blindfold and had taken over where Casey had left off. She could see the anal plug still sticking out of his behind as he plunged into his wife.

'Uh . . . oh Alice . . . baby!'

Alice's arms came around his body and she clutched him feverishly to her, their little game forgotten as they were swept away by a tide of passion which had more to do with love now than lust. Their breathing seemed to combine as they wrestled together, rolling around on the big double bed, oblivious to the fact that they were not alone, uncaring that Pamela and Casey were watching them.

Pamela gazed at them, strangely moved by the joyousness of their coupling after the debauchery that had gone before. It reassured her, made her feel curiously happy, as if she had played some small part in helping them attain the sensual heights to which they were now surging.

'Come on,' Casey whispered, close to her ear, 'let's leave them to it.'

Pamela nodded and stood up, standing acquiescent while Casey straightened her clothes for her and hastily donned her own. She felt drained, dazed by the events of the past hour. With one last look at Alice and Drew, rolling on the bed, racing inexorably to the pinnacle together, she leaned into Casey and allowed her to lead her out of the room.

Chapter Seven

THE FULL MOON slanted its milky rays across the duvet in Jeff and Pamela's bedroom, dappling the patterned fabric with eerie light. Jeff lay, wakeful in the semi-darkness, trying to think of a way of finding Pamela.

He felt angry that she had chosen to run away rather than confront their problems, and his anger compounded his misery. Conveniently putting aside the fact that he had been the one to cause those problems, he battered down his pillow and turned over, determined to get some sleep. He'd never felt so wretched and depressed, and he did not like the feeling. Damn Pamela and her childish temper – he wasn't going to give her the satisfaction of lying sleepless for another whole night!

As if she'd know. The absurdity of his anger made him sigh. Dragging her nightdress over to his pillow so that he could sleep with his cheek against it, Jeff closed his eyes. If only she'd ring again – how could he be sure that she was safe? That nothing had happened to her? Eventually, through sheer exhaustion, he fell asleep.

In his dreams he found himself walking through a garden. It was the kind of garden where one could get lost, where huge, rolling lawns merged with secret gardens and shady bowers, and the spreading branches of mature trees provided shelter from the sun.

It was summertime and the sickly-sweet scent of honeysuckle was heavy on the air. Birdsong, constant, yet not too close, provided background music as he walked along the mosaic-laid stone pathway.

He was looking for something. There was a horrible, sinking feeling in the pit of his stomach, as if he had lost something valuable, yet he knew that, if he hurried, he might find it still.

'Pamela?' His voice seemed loud on the clear, still air, even though he had not raised it.

Looking around, he saw that he was completely alone in the garden, not a single breath disturbed the peace except his own. She had to be here, somewhere.

At the bottom of the lawn there was a rickety, white-painted gate with an arch which was almost completely covered with dog rose. Jeff felt drawn to the gateway, if only because he could not see any other way that she could have gone.

As soon as he stepped through the gate, he heard her laughter drifting on the warm, sweet-scented air. He smiled, his heart lifting at the sound, and his step quickened. Beyond the gate the garden was a maze of winding paths and tall shrubs and hedges. Jeff began to run, round and round in ever decreasing circles.

Pausing as he reached the centre of the spiral, he felt himself tremble, putting off the moment when he would round the corner and see her, like a child who leaves the biggest present under the Christmas tree until last.

As he stepped forward, he saw her at once. She was wearing a bright, buttercup yellow sundress with a full, billowing skirt, the kind of style his mother would have worn in the fifties, and a white sunhat with a huge brim, tied beneath her chin with a wide yellow ribbon which matched her dress.

She was sitting on a swing which was suspended by long, white ropes from the gnarled boughs of an ancient oak tree. As she swung back and forth, her skirt blew up over her knees, giving him a tantalising glimpse of her stocking-tops. Her feet, encased in slender white shoes, flew over his head and back again. In the slipstream of the movement, he could smell her perfume.

Jeff felt his heart fill with a pure, incandescent joy. He wanted to run forward and take her in his arms, to swing with her on the giant swing and feel the breeze blowing past his face, but something kept him rooted to the spot.

Pamela seemed unaware of his presence, looking right through him as she swung back and forth. With a lurch of his belly, Jeff suddenly saw that there were another pair of legs dangling from the seat of the swing, naked legs, strong and hairy, unmistakably masculine.

As Pamela swung back again, she threw back her head, exposing her lovely throat, and her carefree laughter filled the air. Jeff watched as the man on whose lap she was sitting bent his dark head to kiss her neck. The breeze blew up Pamela's skirt again, and Jeff caught a glimpse of her naked sex, bulging with the rigid shaft which was buried inside her.

He was too late. The realisation that someone else had got to her first caused an actual physical pain to shoot through him, so fierce that he doubled up, gasping for breath.

'No!'

Jeff woke up, sweating. Sitting bolt upright in bed, he realised that Pamela's nightdress was tangled about his body and he dragged it roughly away from him. He could not rid himself of the piercing pain that had run through him as he had seen the stranger's penis embedded in Pamela's body. That awful, possessive rage – he shuddered.

What had made him dream such a thing? He was not normally given to superstition, but Jeff could not shake off a horrible feeling of foreboding as he lay back down again. He had to find her, to speak to her. She had to know that he didn't want to lose her, before it was too late. Perhaps it was too late already? No – he could not allow himself

114

to think that! Pamela loved him, he was sure of it. Surely all the happy years they had spent together would count for something?

His sister-in-law, Tiffany, would be back the day after next. She'd tell him where Pamela had gone. Pushing away the certainty that Tiffany would do no such thing unless Pamela had told her to, Jeff lay back and closed his eyes again. Knowing that there would be no more sleep for him that night, he settled for rest instead, waiting without enthusiasm for the onset of dawn.

As they walked along the endless corridors of Elysium Hall, Pamela slowly became aware of the weight of Casey's arm around her shoulders and the lithe, graceful length of her body walking in concert with hers. She had seen her give such pleasure to Alice, giving so selflessly, and she realised that, whilst both she and Alice, and Drew, for that matter, had all gained sexual fulfilment, Casey had been left unsatisfied.

A tentative shiver of anticipation rippled through her as she imagined giving Casey that satisfaction herself. Could she do it?

Casey's room was nearer to the Slatterys' than Pamela's, and they both paused outside. Casey turned the key in the lock before glancing at Pamela.

'Would you like to come in for a drink?'

Her voice was low and husky, infinitely seductive. Pamela swallowed hard and took a leap into the unknown.

'I'd like to come in,' she said, 'but not for a drink.'

Casey looked at her for a moment as if she was wondering if she'd misheard her. When Pamela merely gazed steadily back at her, her pupils dilated and her eyelids drooped slightly. Pamela recognised the slow-burning excitement gathering momentum, sensed the tension in the other girl's body and felt a rush of power the like of which she had never experienced before. Suddenly she was impatient and it was she who opened the door.

Casey's bedroom was the antithesis of Pamela's. There was no tasteful peach or eau-de-Nil here, only rich ruby red with splashes of gold and black. The furniture was of a stark, geometric, thoroughly modern design, the bed a king-sized symphony of red silk with gold satin pillows piled high.

Pamela turned to Casey and raised her eyebrows. 'This room shouldn't suit anybody – so why is it so perfect for you?'

Casey laughed, slipping off her shoes and kicking them across the gold carpet. Without the ludicrously high heels she favoured she was only slightly taller than Pamela.

'It's totally over the top, isn't it? They always put me in here – I love it!'

She gave a little twirl in the centre of the room, holding out her arms as if to embrace the room itself. Pamela's eyes followed the line of her body, admiring its taut, well-toned profile, the skin moving over sculpted muscle. As she came to face her, Casey caught her eye and Pamela sucked in her breath. There was no laughter in Casey's face now, just a stark, unconcealed desire which frightened Pamela almost as much as it thrilled her.

'Casey . . .' she whispered, suddenly finding it difficult to talk, 'Casey, I've never . . .' She shook her head, impatient with the way the words had suddenly abandoned her.

'I know, honey,' Casey said, moving forward so that they were standing toe to toe.

Pamela could smell her perfume, overlaying the fainter, no less evocative scents of fresh perspiration and the lingering trace of the secretions from Alice's body. Her smooth, black skin shone dully in the soft light of the bedside lamps, and Pamela reached out, unable to resist the urge to run her fingertip slightly across the curve of her shoulder. It felt like fine velvet.

'You'll have to show me,' she breathed, running her fingers along the line of Casey's collarbone, 'help me . . .'

Without saying a word, Casey reached behind her and unfastened her dress. As she allowed it to slither down her body to the floor, Pamela's eyes followed its progress, eager to see the other girl's body revealed as it had been before. She was wearing a matching bra and brief set in slate blue lace. As Pamela watched, she slid the straps of the bra off her shoulders and her fingers hovered over the front fastener.

Glancing up at her, Pamela saw the question in her dark brown eyes. Pamela's fingers trembled as she touched the gentle swell of Casey's small breasts, feeling the firm, springy flesh as she slid her fingers towards the opening of the bra. Never in her wildest imaginings had she ever seen herself taking off another woman's underwear, but she had to admit that she was more excited now than she had ever been when unwrapping a male body. Perhaps it was merely the novelty of something new . . .? Pamela did not care as she slowly peeled the cups away from Casey's breasts. She only knew that, at that moment at least, it was all she wanted to do.

She felt a thrill of pleasure as she saw that the other girl's nipples were already erect. Like two perfect, dark berries they puckered enticingly and Pamela felt a pulse begin to beat between her legs.

Casey stood, acquiescent, as Pamela pushed the bra down her arms before casting it aside. Tempting though she found Casey's exposed breasts, Pamela knew that she wanted her completely naked before she touched her. And yet she didn't want it to be over too soon.

Conscious that Casey was deliberately allowing her to set the pace, Pamela ran the palms of her hands across the soft lace, reaching behind her to cup her tight buttocks before brushing across the front panel. The feel of her mound of Venus was quite delicious, and for the first time Pamela experienced what a man must feel when he first touches a woman. Excited, certainly, but she hadn't expected that feeling to be tinged with such awe.

Glancing to gauge Casey's reaction, Pamela saw that her face was expressionless, her eyes staring straight ahead. Only the slight flare of her nostrils and the rapid little breaths escaping through her softly parted lips betrayed her inner agitation.

Slowly, tentatively, Pamela allowed her fingertips to creep lower. Her own sex felt warm, the lips swelling and moistening as she encountered the damp gusset. This blatant evidence of Casey's arousal drove her wild with wanting, driving what little rational thoughts she still entertained straight from her head.

Hooking her thumbs in the waistband of the panties, Pamela dragged them almost roughly down the length of Casey's strong, smooth-skinned thighs, bending down to help her step out of them. As she straightened again, she caught the unmistakable scent of female arousal and she shivered, almost overcome by excitement.

Their eyes met and Pamela saw that Casey's were now two dark whirlpools of emotion, sucking her in, inviting her to drown with her. Fleetingly, Pamela worried that she didn't know what to do, had no clue as to the mechanics of sex with another woman.

As if sensing her dilemma, Casey picked up one of Pamela's hands, and placed it, palm down, over her left breast.

'Can you feel my heart beating?' she whispered.

Pamela nodded, drawing strength from the strong, steady rhythm. Casey's skin was warm and moist, the tight little crest digging into the centre of her palm. Slowly, tentatively, she began to move her flattened hand in a circle, round and round, polishing the hard little nub until Casey let out a small, involuntary groan.

Gaining in confidence, Pamela cupped the right breast in her other hand and squeezed gently, kneading the taut flesh in her fingers, watching in fascination as the nipple hardened and little beads of perspiration began to push through Casey's pores.

She could feel the tightly leashed passion in the other girl's body. Knowing that Casey was trying to hold back for her made caressing her all the more thrilling. Feeling her tremble beneath her touch gave Pamela such a feeling of erotic power that she almost came, there and then.

With a sigh which drifted across Casey's heated skin, she bent her head and touched the tip of first one nipple, then the other, with her tongue. The skin tasted slightly salty, with an underlying sweetness which Pamela knew must be the unique taste of Casey's skin. Hungry for more, she enclosed one nub with her lips and suckled on it.

The nipple and its surrounding areola seemed to feed itself into her mouth, the flesh quivering with a life of its own as it moved in and out.

Swirling her tongue around the tip, then drawing deeply on the teat, Pamela stimulated the breast with a milking action which was clearly driving Casey to the brink. With her free hand, she squeezed and rolled the other breast, playing with the nipple and pinching it between finger and thumb.

Casey moaned deep in her throat and swayed towards Pamela. Placing her hands on her shoulders, she leaned on her, her breath coming in rapid gasps as Pamela's sucking became deeper, pulling on the invisible thread, the nerve line, which joins the nipples to the womb.

'Oh, baby!' she cried as the pre-orgasmic tremors ran through her. 'Harder ... yes! Oh yes!' She threw back her head and laughed aloud, a long, joyous sound that made Pamela's heart give a little leap.

Casey's legs buckled under her and she sank elegantly on to the carpet, taking Pamela with her. Pam gazed at the tumescent breast, shiny with saliva, and waited for Casey to catch her breath. Had she really brought the other girl to orgasm just by sucking her breast? she marvelled, inordinately proud of her unexpected prowess.

Casey reached up and stroked her face tenderly. Reading the pride which must have been written all over her face, she smiled. 'Be naked for me, honey,' she said huskily.

Pamela had forgotten that she was still fully clothed and she hastened to comply with Casey's request. Her fingers shook as she stripped, and she was conscious of the other girl watching her, as she had watched Casey before. Did Casey feel the same sense of anticipation, the same breathless excitement that she had felt then?

Her own body seemed impossibly white and fleshy in comparison, but Casey seemed to find it attractive. She reached out and stroked each area: her chest, her breasts, her stomach, her thighs. Casey's long fingers brushed over her pubis before fluttering down to her thighs. Each touch was featherlight, a butterfly caress which served merely to accentuate Pamela's already over-sensitised senses.

When she was naked, they both rose and climbed on to the big double bed. Pamela was shivering, from nerves and from an excess of emotion. Noticing this, Casey lifted the light-weight duvet and pulled it up around their shoulders. She made no attempt to touch Pamela in a sexual way again, she merely cuddled her close, waiting for her to be ready to continue.

Pamela could not ever remember feeling so *safe* in another person's arms, except, maybe, in the early days of her marriage to Jeff. But even then, she realised now, there was always a deep, atavistic knowledge that he was the stronger one, that if he so chose he could physically dominate her. He wasn't that kind of man, but nevertheless, just the fact that the *potential* was there meant that there was always a primitive kind of tension between them.

With Casey Pamela felt as if the balance of

power was more equal, that if one should want to dominate the other, it would have to be an act which was wholly consensual. The feel of another woman's body close to hers was unnerving, but pleasantly so. It was like lying next to herself, making love to herself, her alter ego, perhaps. Pamela smiled to herself. How narcissistic!

She closed her eyes and rested her cheek against Casey's breasts for a moment. It was such a close, intimate position that slowly, gradually, Pamela's skin began to prickle with awareness everywhere the other woman's skin touched.

'Okay, honey?' Casey asked after a few minutes.

She sounded sleepy, as if still enveloped by the glow caused by her recent orgasm. Pamela lifted her head and smiled at her in the semi-darkness.

'Make love to me, Casey. Show me how it can be between two women.'

Casey bent her head and touched her lips gently against Pamela's. They were so soft and full, so intrinsically *feminine*, that Pamela felt herself turn liquid at the mere thought of what she was doing. Wrapping her arms around the other girl's body, she encouraged her to deepen the kiss, welcoming the probe of her tongue and the sudden, shocking nip of her teeth against the tender flesh of her inner lip.

They lay, locked together, breast to breast, belly to belly, hip to hip, mouths grinding against teeth, for several minutes. When Casey finally broke off the kiss, Pamela was left gasping for air, her whole body trembling in reaction.

123

After a moment, she realised that Casey was no longer accepting the passive role. Her hands smoothed and caressed Pamela's skin, moving from arm to breasts to thighs to stomach so rapidly that Pamela hardly knew where to expect her touch next. Soon her entire body was tingling, electrified, it seemed, by Casey's touch.

Pamela lay back against the silk-covered pillows, allowing Casey to arrange her limbs any way she pleased, floating on a tide of sensation which was growing in intensity all the time. She gasped as her breasts were gathered up in Casey's sensitive hands and pushed together so that she could lick from one to the other so rapidly that it felt as though she was tasting both at the same time.

Through the dense fog of her arousal, Pamela realised that she was writhing on the bed, virtually begging to be given release, like a sex-crazed beast, without control. Spreading her legs, she braced her bare feet against the sheet so that she could thrust her pelvis upward, making her needs known.

Casey chuckled, deep in her throat.

'Steady, baby, steady!' she crooned, her long fingernails scoring lightly down Pamela's mid-line, coming to rest at the edge of her pubic hair. 'We've got all night, no need to rush. Hey, hey . . .' She kissed her as Pamela moaned in protest.

'Please . . .!'

'What is it? You want this?' Casey bent her

head and nibbled gently on a nipple, laughing softly as Pamela shook her head from side to side.

'No? This then . . .' She nuzzled the warm valley between her breasts and bent to flick her tongue into her navel.

Pamela's response was to strain her hips further up, trying to make Casey's lips make contact with her pubis, but Casey refused to acknowledge her need.

'Oh honey, your skin tastes so good, I could lick and kiss you like this all night!'

'Casey!' Pamela gasped, grasping the other woman by the shoulders and trying ineffectually to urge her downward. 'Please, please stop teasing! I'll die for sure if you don't let me come soon!'

'Patience, Pammie. I like to save the honeypot till last . . . savoury before sweet, y'know? Relax now . . . I'm about ready for my dessert . . .'

Pamela thought she might swoon clear away as, at last, Casey's long fingers ran delicately along the channels of her sex.

'Mmmm . . . oh honey, you're *so-o* wet! Is this all for me?'

She slipped her middle finger into Pamela's body, moving it round in slow, teasing circles before withdrawing it and smearing her juices along the wet, puffy labia, up to her clitoris. At the first touch of her fingers there, Pamela cried aloud, certain she would come at once. But Casey was too experienced to allow that to happen, and she immediately went back to exploring her body with her fingertips.

Stroking around Pamela's spread sex, she drew some of the moisture down over her perineum and to the pouting mouth of her anus. Pamela's automatic reflex was to clench her buttocks tight and Casey's chuckle reverberated against her ear.

'Relax, baby, open up for me.'

As she spoke, she used the first and second fingers of one hand to separate the two halves of Pamela's sex. At the same time, she moved down Pamela's body and pushed her long, wet tongue into her vagina.

Pamela whimpered and gyrated her hips, unable to control her reaction. She had not expected it to feel so good; Casey knew exactly what rhythm to use, what depth to plunge into her. Her clever tongue sent Pamela into a paroxysm of pleasure so that when she jabbed teasingly at her anus, she forgot to tense up, earning herself a long, slow lick of approval from her vagina to her clitoris.

Casey lifted her head briefly to smile at Pamela. Pam could see her own juices glistening on the other girl's chin and she was glad of the muted lighting so that she could mask her reaction to the sight. The intense, almost animalistic surge of feeling she experienced was shocking, elemental. Casey grinned at her, knowing full well what was going through her mind.

'Mmmm,' she said mischievously. 'Yum yum!'

Then she dived back between Pamela's thighs and went to work on her clitoris in earnest. First she swirled her tongue with infuriating gentleness round and round the hard little button, never actually touching it, but causing it to quiver with pleasure. After a few seconds, she slipped her hands underneath Pamela so that she was gripping her by the buttocks. Lifting her slightly, she moved her head from side to side, lashing the tiny bundle of nerves lightly with the very tip of her tongue.

Pamela could feel the tight knot of tension which had been building in her stomach spreading through the lower half of her body. Her legs felt leaden, useless to her as all her perception of sensation was focused on that one small area which Casey was now licking with a sure, steady rhythm which was gradually gaining momentum.

Closing her eyes, Pamela arched her neck and closed her hands into fists. Her entire body seemed to be on the brink of explosion as Casey flicked, faster and faster, and Pamela knew that there would be no turning back now. She would come, and soon, yet it would not be enough. She'd want this again, and again and again.

It came then, sweeping over her like a blanket of heat, making her cry out, not caring who heard her.

'Yes! Oh God! Yes! Casey . . .!'

The sensations peaked, then began to subside. This was the point at which Jeff would come inside her, fill her with his maleness and join her at the peak. If she had thought she would miss it, she was surprised, for Casey did not move away.

Her tongue slowed and gentled, but she did not remove it from its target.

Pamela wriggled slightly, but Casey kept a firm grip on her buttocks and would not let her squirm away. Just as she was about to protest, she began to tongue her again, coaxing the softening bud back to hardness and, incredibly, Pamela felt the glow begin again.

This time her orgasm rolled over her in mellow waves, bathing her in heat, and rippling right down to her toes. Pamela stretched out her legs, wanting the lovely, languorous feeling to go on forever.

She smiled at Casey as she finally surfaced, a smile full of affection and gratitude. Filled with a burning desire to afford her the same compliment, Pamela eased her hand between Casey's legs and cupped her sex. It was hot and wet, tempting her.

'Oh honey,' Casey whispered hoarsely as Pamela found her burgeoning clitoris, 'it would be good. But once you taste pussy you'll be lost!'

Pamela grinned and kissed Casey full on the lips.

'I'm already lost,' she murmured, slipping down beneath the covers.

She hadn't known what to expect and was pleasantly surprised to realise, after the first tentative dabs with her tongue against the other girl's intimate flesh, that she liked the taste. It was unlike anything she had ever tasted before, neither sweet nor sour, simply unique.

Quickly growing in confidence, she caressed and tantalised the fleshy lips of Casey's sex until the other girl was moaning with pleasure. Her clitoris emerged gradually from its covering, swelling and hardening as Casey's excitement grew. Pamela began to concentrate her efforts there, progressing from light, long licks to smaller, harder jabs. Using the flat of her tongue she moved the skin around the shiny little bead, knowing how exquisite yet infuriating such a caress could be.

All the time she was imagining how she would feel if she was the recipient of her caresses. Casey's entire body thrummed with tension now. Pamela could feel her clitoris pulsing and she lashed it with her tongue, knowing instinctively that Casey needed the extra pressure to tip her over.

When she began to buck her hips, Pamela hammered her tongue quite roughly against it before sipping greedily at the lip of her vagina where the love-juice overflowed at the point of climax.

Exhausted, they lay back on the bed, their bare, damp limbs intertwined, the taste of each other on their lips, oblivious to the tender light of dawn pushing its way through the gap in the curtains. Staring into Casey's eyes, kissing occasionally, Pamela marvelled at the sheer joy of what they had shared. And as the birds began to sing outside the window, they fell asleep, still entwined.

Chapter Eight

IT WAS ALMOST lunchtime before they woke, giggling like naughty schoolgirls as they realised the time.

'Let's call room service and we'll take a shower while they send up breakfast,' Casey suggested as they untangled themselves from the sheets.

'Okay. You order while I go to the bathroom,' Pamela agreed.

She had expected to feel uncomfortable, confronting the events of the night before in the cold light of day, but in fact she felt more relaxed than she had for a long while. Standing under a stream of warm water, she closed her eyes and replayed the experiences she had shared with Casey. It had been so exciting, yet also so intrinsically loving that Pamela knew she could have no regrets.

Opening her eyes, she smiled as Casey joined her in the shower, moving over in the small cubicle so that she could share the spray. Picking up the shower gel, she lathered some between her hands and began to soap Casey's body, lingering at all the places she had loved the night before. The feelings she had experienced then echoed through her body, muted now, but still thrilling.

Casey must have felt it too, for she turned slowly until she was facing Pamela and took her into her arms. Her wet, soapy skin was slippery against Pamela's as she rubbed herself suggestively against her. Taking the shower gel from her hand, she returned the compliment, lathering Pamela's body so that they could both stand beneath the hot spray and rinse off together.

When all the soap had disappeared down the plug-hole, Casey turned the dial on the shower and Pamela squealed as a deluge of cold water poured over her breasts, rolling across her stomach and down her legs.

'Oh! How could you!'

Casey laughed, stepping out of the cubicle and holding out a huge, fluffy towel for Pamela to dry herself with.

'It's good for you, honey – I always end my shower with a cold dousing.'

'Well bully for you!' Pamela replied, thoroughly disgruntled. 'Remind me never to take a shower with you again!'

Casey laughed, giving herself a brisk rub-down with her towel before throwing it in the corner of the room.

'C'mon, Pammie – you can drip-dry the rest!'

She made a grab for Pamela's towel which she was attempting to fasten around her breasts and threw it over to where she had abandoned her own.

'Casey!' Pamela protested mildly, but the other girl merely laughed. 'Humour me,' she coaxed. 'I like looking at you.'

'Over breakfast?' Pamela laughed.

Casey leaned forward and leered theatrically at her.

'*Especially* over breakfast!' she said.

They were both laughing as they walked into the bedroom, though Pamela's grin froze on her face when she saw the waiter at the end of the bed. She didn't know who was the more shocked: her to walk into the bedroom and find him there, or him. Judging by the look of astonishment on his face as he saw them, coming face to face with two naked women still damp from the shower was a novel experience for him.

His eyes slithered from them to the still rumpled bedclothes and back again, realisation dawning as clearly as if he was a cartoon character parodying disbelief. He held the tray poised in mid air, his mouth was open.

Pamela stifled a giggle behind her hand. Casey being Casey, it was she who took charge.

'Well, well, what have we here?' she drawled, completely unfazed. 'Lift your chin up from the floor, baby, before you trip over it.'

The man immediately snapped his mouth closed and, flustered, placed the tray firmly on the coffee table.

'I'm sorry, ladies – I thought you must have heard my knock. I'll just leave this here for you, shall I?' he said.

After his initial dumbfounded reaction, he seemed to have pulled himself together and was trying his damnedest to act as though being in a confined space with two naked women was a commonplace occurrence to him. Pamela watched as Casey sat down on the edge of the bed and lounged on to one elbow. Her small breasts swung softly to one side and Pamela saw that, despite his feigned nonchalance, the waiter could not take his eyes off them.

'Did you knock?' Casey asked innocently. 'Gee, I'm sorry – we were kinda busy in the shower . . . know what I mean?'

A dull flush crept beneath the young man's skin and Pamela saw that the front of his trousers were straining across a not inconsiderable erection. The atmosphere in the room was suddenly thick with tension and she breathed shallowly, intrigued to know what Casey would do next.

As Pamela watched from the doorway of the bathroom, Casey rolled on to her stomach, lifting the upper half of her body off the bed and leaning on her elbows while her feet bent up behind her, crossed at the ankles.

'What's your name, hon?'

'Michael, ma'am.'

' "Michael ma'am"?' Casey mimicked playfully. 'Well, "Michael ma'am", since you're here, why don't you stay and take breakfast with us?'

She glanced across at Pamela and winked as the young man's head shot up in astonishment.

'Oh, I don't think I could do that, I—' he broke off abruptly and his adam's apple bobbed once as Casey slithered along the length of the bed towards him, hauling herself along by her arms.

'Do stay,' she husked, pouting invitingly.

Michael glanced uncertainly at Pamela and she smiled at him. He was rather an attractive youth with long, sun-bleached hair pulled into an untidy ponytail. His face was angular and quite long and there were white lines around his eyes which suggested he spent a lot of time outside, squinting in the sun. His eyes were the colour of a cloudy day, stormy now, as if he couldn't quite believe his luck, but knew he was out of his depth.

'Take a chance, Michael,' Pamela said gently, speaking for the first time. 'Where's the harm?'

The tip of his tongue pushed through his lips as he regarded her and he moistened them, licking at the film of sweat which had broken out on his upper lip.

'He looks awful hot, Pam – why don't you help him take that shirt off while I lay out breakfast?'

Pamela moved forward, aware of his eyes on her nakedness. Strangely, she did not feel self-conscious – rather she lifted her chin and deliberately put a swing in her walk, proud of her body in a way she had never been before.

Michael did not move as she approached him, though she could sense his tension as he waited for her to touch him. He stood, passive as a statue as she reached out and began to unfasten the pristine white shirt which was regulation dress for all the waiting staff at Elysium Hall.

His skin felt damp as the backs of her fingers brushed against it and she realised that he was struggling to keep his reactions in check. His hands were balled into fists at his side, as if he didn't trust himself not to touch her, and wasn't sure that it was permissible.

This kind of domination was much more exciting to Pamela than that in which she had participated the night before. Seeing Drew Slattery bound and restrained, at the mercy of his wife and anyone else she saw fit to grant dominion over him, was far less of a thrill than sensing this young man's barely leashed passion now. There were no chains to restrain him, he was in thrall to his own lust. The fact that that lust was partly for her gave Pamela a kick she had never felt even while wielding the crop over Drew.

Glancing at Casey, Pamela saw that she had discarded the warm croissants and muesli and had set out a large jug of cream and some strawberry jam on the tray. A bowl of freshly hulled strawberries was by her side and as Pamela watched, she popped one between her lips. A small dribble of fruit juice escaped through her lips and ran down her chin and Pamela had to suppress the urge to go over and catch it with her tongue. As if reading her thoughts, Casey wiped her chin with the back of her hand and licked the juice herself, holding Pamela's eye and smiling as she did so.

'Take his shirt off,' she said softly, dipping her long forefinger into the cream and sucking on the end.

Pamela did as she was asked, aware that watching Casey's blatantly seductive display had re-awakened her sleeping sex. It throbbed gently between her legs, anticipating attention.

Michael's upper body was as tanned as his face, well-shaped in a pleasing inverted triangle and smooth, so smooth that Pamela wondered whether he shaved his chest hair.

'You look like you work out,' she murmured, running her hands appreciatively across the firm slabs of muscle beneath his nipples.

'I surf,' he said, his voice thick. 'You have to be strong.'

'Good,' Casey said, laughter in her voice. 'Do you think you're strong enough to make love to two women at the same time?'

Michael swallowed again, but his eyes glittered with a wholly masculine pride which told them he would only be their plaything for as long as *he* chose.

'I think so,' he replied.

Casey knelt up on the bed and, reaching over the tray of breakfast things, she traced a finger from the point where his collarbones met, down his midline to his navel, then further down to the waistband of his regulation black trousers.

'Strip for us then.'

The two women watched as Michael hastily removed what remained of his clothing. Pamela's breath hurt in her chest as she watched the tanned, curiously hairless body emerge: strong, muscular legs, straight, sturdy feet, tightly moulded buttocks. And a cock which was as golden as the rest of him, long and slender and fully erect, the circumcised tip pointing straight upwards.

With his tan and his carefully built-up body, depilated, she now saw, all over apart from between his legs, he reminded Pamela of a statue of a Greek god. On an impulse, she reached forward and freed his hair from its ponytail so that it could ripple unimpeded across his shoulders.

He stood there, posing for them until Pamela thought that they would all snap under the tension.

'Nice body, Michael,' Casey said softly, smiling at Pamela as he preened visibly. 'Don't you think he looks good enough to eat, Pammie?'

Pamela smiled as she saw the way Casey's mind was working and she moved up close to Michael so that she could murmur in his ear, 'Oh yes, Casey – definitely good enough to eat!'

He shivered as her warm breath tickled across his skin and her soft breasts flattened against the hard contours of his back. Casey rose up slowly from the bed. She picked up the jug of cream and came round to Pamela. Holding her eye, she tipped the jug slightly so that the cold liquid trickled on to Michael's skin, pooling in the dip of his collarbone. Michael gasped, but stood very, very still as Pamela moved round to lap it up with her tongue.

All the time she was doing this, Pamela kept her eyes locked on to Casey's. She could see the other girl was turned on, that she was merely using the beautiful young man between them as a conductor for her passion. And although Pamela was physically caressing Michael, it was Casey to whom she was really making love.

Casey tipped the jug again and this time the cream ran in little, viscous rivulets down his chest. Pamela caught them on her tongue, dabbing quickly at them, tasting the salty tang of his skin. He trembled as her breasts brushed softly against the tip of his penis, all too briefly.

'What do you like to eat for breakfast, Casey?' she asked, keeping her tone conversational.

Casey held her gaze, her dark eyes smouldering in an otherwise impassive face. 'Oh, I have a sweet tooth. I like honey,' she purred.

Pamela smiled, teasing her. 'I think strawberry jam will have to suffice this morning, darling,' she said, exalting in the flare of surprise which lit up the other girl's eyes as she took the initiative away from her for the first time. 'Come and kneel down here at Michael's feet while I prepare breakfast for you.'

She watched as Casey complied, admiring the dark, flawless ebony of her skin in contrast to the golden sheen of Michael's. It was a contradiction, seeing Casey take the submissive role, knowing how assertive she was normally. Yet Pamela could see that this reversal of roles had affected the other girl: her pupils were dilated and she watched Pamela with a curiously intense expression as she waited to see what she would do.

Pamela picked up the dish of strawberry jam and scooped some up on her fingers. Sucking it between her lips she let the sweet, sticky substance coat her mouth, twirling her tongue along the insides of her cheeks. Two pairs of eyes were transfixed, watching her, and she felt a little thrill of excitement.

Moving forward, she encircled Michael's penis with her hand and ran it up and down the shaft several times. The skin was silky soft over the hard core and it twitched slightly against her palm.

'You have a beautiful cock, Michael,' she told him.

'Thank you,' he gulped and Pamela smiled.

'Don't you think so, Casey? Infinitely kissable.'

Reaching for the dish again she scooped up a generous dollop of strawberry jam and ran his penis through it, smearing it with the red jelly. Glancing at Casey kneeling quietly at her feet, she offered Michael's jam-smeared penis to her.

'Breakfast,' she whispered.

Holding her eye, Casey moved forward and

parted her lips, kneeling passively as Pamela fed Michael's sticky penis into her mouth. Her cheeks bulged as he filled them and Pamela caressed Casey's face, feeling him inside her.

Michael was panting now, his control almost gone. Casey closed her eyes, enjoying him, and Pamela knelt down beside her so that she could watch. It was a beautiful sight, the long, firm cock, cleaned now of the strawberry jam which had covered it, sliding gracefully in and out of Casey's soft mouth.

Pamela leaned forward and kissed Casey's face before resting her lips next to the corner of her mouth so that she could feel Michael moving. Poking out her tongue, she felt the rigid shaft, wet with Casey's saliva, run along it, back and forth.

Reaching down between Casey's thighs, she found the warm, wet centre of her and began to rub up and down her labia. Timing her movements to coincide with Michael's, she felt the tension build in Casey's clitoris until she wanted nothing more than to see her come.

Michael cried out as his seed began to pump along his shaft and into Casey's greedy mouth. As she swallowed, Pamela increased the pressure of her fingertips against her clitoris so that, seconds after Michael climaxed, Casey joined him.

Frantic by now, Pamela clutched at her own pulsing sex and quickly brought herself to crisis point so that the three of them collapsed against each other, laughing, on the deep pile carpet at the end of the bed.

After a few minutes, Casey invited Michael to stay and have breakfast with them.

'I'm sorry, ladies,' he said, genuine regret colouring his voice, 'but I've probably already been missed in the kitchens. I like this job too much to risk it – especially the little extras!' He grinned cheekily at them.

Casey and Pamela climbed into bed together and watched appreciatively as he pulled on his clothes. There was something perversely erotic about watching a man dress. Hungry now, Pamela split open a croissant and began to smear it with butter and strawberry jam. Michael watched her, beginning to stiffen again.

'I don't think I'll ever be able to look at a dish of strawberry jam again without getting an erection,' he said ruefully.

Pamela and Casey both laughed, blowing him kisses as he scurried out of the door.

'Did you enjoy that, honey?' Casey asked her conversationally as she poured them both coffee.

'Mmm. You looked so gorgeous with your mouth full! Actually, it set me thinking about Jeff.'

'Gee, thanks!' Casey drawled, making Pamela laugh.

'Sorry. It's just . . . well, you know how when we first met you said I should use this opportunity to broaden my own sexual horizons?'

'Uh-huh,' Casey said through a mouthful of croissant crumbs.

'Well, I've certainly done that! And you were right, it *has* made me see things in a different light. I would like us to work things out, if we can.'

'But?'

'But there's something else I have to work through.'

'Want to tell me about it?'

Pamela settled herself more comfortably against the pillows and sipped thoughtfully at her coffee.

'When I saw Jeff with Dena, I was devastated, obviously. But ... that wasn't all I felt ...' her voice trailed away as she remembered.

'Did it turn you on, honey? Seeing your man making it with another girl?'

Pamela gazed at Casey, taken aback by her perceptiveness.

Casey laughed gently at her. 'It's not so shocking, you know – a lot of women fantasise about watching the old man giving it to another woman.'

'They do?'

'Sure. Not that most of them would want it to actually happen, like it did with you, but as far as fantasies go, it's a pretty good one. And harmless too, if it stays a fantasy.'

'But that's just it, isn't it?' Pamela said bitterly. 'In my case it was all too real.'

Casey leaned over and kissed her gently on the lips.

'So how do you propose to work it out?'

Pamela frowned.

'I don't know. That is ... it's happened, you

know? I can't change that. And being turned on by it . . . well, it cheapened me, at least that's what I felt.'

'So?'

'So, maybe if it happened again, if I was in control this time . . . I don't know – am I making any sense at all?'

Casey helped herself to a bowl of strawberries and cream and popped a spoonful into Pamela's mouth. The cool, pulpy fruit slipped down her throat and she opened her mouth for more.

'Let me get this straight,' Casey said, feeding her another spoonful. 'You want to set Jeff up with another woman so that you can watch them together.'

Pamela nodded, feeling slightly embarrassed.

'And then?'

'I don't know. Maybe once I've worked through the fantasy, the two of us will stand a chance of starting over again.'

'Or maybe you'll be overcome with rage and jealousy and kill this other girl!'

'Not if it was you, I wouldn't.'

The two women looked at each other steadily, each considering the possibilities. It was Casey who broke the loaded silence.

'Honey, I'd be happy to help out, but I'm only in the country until the end of the week.'

'I could see if I could get him to come here.'

'Would he come, do you think?'

'I think so. He sounded as though he'd try anything.'

143

'And would you tell him about the "therapy" you've got planned for him when he gets here?'

Pamela smiled. 'I don't think so. He probably wouldn't understand,' she explained.

'I don't know, honey – is that really being fair to him?'

'Casey! What does playing fair have to do with anything? He's hardly been fair to me, has he? He *owes* me!'

Casey regarded her thoughtfully for a few minutes, a worried frown creasing her forehead. 'Are you sure you could handle it?'

'I don't know. But I'd like to try.'

'I guess you'd better ring him, then.'

Pamela smiled. 'I will. But not just yet . . .'

She leaned across and kissed Casey lingeringly on the mouth. Her full, moist lips opened hungrily beneath hers and they came together, wrapping their arms around each other and sliding down the bed. Pamela ran her hands down the sides of Casey's body, rediscovering every line and curve and revelling in the satiny texture of her skin. 'I shall miss you when you go,' she whispered.

'Hush, honey – I told you, didn't I? I come over every year, at least twice.'

Pamela broke away so that she could see her face. Casey was smiling at her, and the expression in her eyes was tender. A rush of affection overwhelmed Pamela and she felt emotional tears prick her eyelids.

'We'll stay friends, then?' she whispered.

'Always,' Casey promised. '*Special* friends.'

Reaching up, she tangled her fingers in the hair at Pamela's nape and pulled her face down to hers.

Chapter Nine

THE RAIN FELL in torrents as Jeff made his way along the motorway, reducing visibility so much that he was forced to slow down. The night was dark and starless, a sliver of moon so slight that it was no more than a muted glow peeking occasionally from between the heavy clouds. A virtual convoy of HGVs on the inside lane sent up a continual spray as he inched his way past them, so that his windscreen wipers were hard pressed to keep up with the deluge of water.

After the restless night, punctured by disturbing dreams, Jeff had felt like death warmed over when the alarm finally went off. Hauling himself into work, he had seen to it that the bare essentials required to keep his business afloat were being taken care of by Dena and his site foreman. Then he gave up on the day and went home again.

As far as he could recall from what Pamela had

told him, Tiffany and Mick were due home from Paris this evening. Like a drowning man, he had hung on to that small scrap of hope throughout the day, hanging around the house, waiting in vain for the silent telephone to ring.

He knew that Mick and Tiffany would no doubt be tired and want to do nothing more than to slump in front of the TV after their flight home. The last thing they'd want was an unexpected house guest. But this was an emergency, dammit, and he hoped they would understand the intrusion.

Turning off the motorway at last, he followed the signs towards central London. Only now did he begin to worry about the reception he might get from his sister-in-law. How much had Pamela told her about their difficulties? Knowing how close the two sisters were, Jeff guessed that she would know everything. With a sigh, he steeled himself for further humiliation.

Tiffany did not disappoint him. Recovering quickly from the shock of finding him standing dripping on her doorstep in the dark, her eyes narrowed and she planted her fists firmly on her hips.

'Jeff, you little turd – what the hell are you doing here?'

'Hello, Tiff,' he said meekly, wincing as she avoided his usual kiss. 'Are you going to let me come in?'

'Give me one good reason why I should.'

Jeff shrugged, his best little-boy-lost expression

firmly in place.

'It's pouring with rain, it feels like I've been driving for hours, I'm your brother-in-law and you love me—' Tiffany snorted and Jeff's face crumpled '—Because I feel like the worst type of shit and I need your help to put things right.'

'That's getting more like it,' Tiffany snapped, though she still didn't move from the doorway.

'Who is it, sweetheart?'

Jeff looked over her shoulder hopefully as Mick's voice boomed from the living-room. The rain was running down the back of his neck now, compounding his misery, and he was beginning to think that Tiffany really was going to send him away. He grinned sheepishly as Mick came into the hallway. Mick took one look at Jeff's grey face and took charge.

'Oh, it's you. For Christ's sake come in then – you're letting the rain in!'

Tiffany walked inside and Jeff stepped gratefully over the threshold as Mick closed the door behind him. Mick looked him up and down and saw that he was dripping on the carpet.

'You'd better get straight upstairs and take a shower. Have you brought a case?'

'Yeah – only it's in the car. I wasn't sure whether you'd be back.'

Mick made a face. 'Well, I'm not going out in this to fetch your bag. I'll find you a spare pair of my pyjamas. If you hurry up I'll even make you some tea and toast.'

'Thanks, mate,' Jeff said as he went up the stairs.

'Don't thank me yet,' Mick said ominously. 'For the record, I happen to agree with Tiff – you've been a prize turd.'

'I know,' muttered Jeff as he ran up the stairs. 'The worst of it is, I'm inclined to agree too.'

Downstairs, Tiffany glared angrily at her husband. 'Where is he?'

'Taking a shower. We couldn't leave him on the doorstep, love – he's family.'

'For how much longer?' she asked snappily.

Mick sighed. 'C'mon, Tiff – give the guy a chance.'

He saw that it was the wrong thing to say as soon as the words fell from his lips.

'How can you say that? You saw how upset Pamela was! If we hadn't sent her off to Elysium Hall, goodness knows what she would have done – she was distraught!'

'I know, I know. But the very fact he's here shows that he's sorry. Everyone's entitled to make a mistake at some time, Tiffany,' he admonished her gently. 'After all – not everyone is lucky enough to spend a weekend each year at Elysium.'

To his relief, Tiffany's face softened as she thought of their annual foray into the turbulent sexual waters of Elysium Hall. She rose and came to stand by him, wrapping her arms around his waist.

'Just remember, Mick, my love – if you ever make the kind of mistake Jeff made with Pamela, you'll have to start sleeping in armour!'

149

Mick winced. 'There's trust for you!' He unlinked her hands from round his waist and kissed her affectionately on the tip of her nose.

She smiled at him, a smile filled with such guileless promise that he felt his toes curl. Even after eight years of marriage, she had the ability to turn his legs to jelly with one look. One of the things he had always liked most about Tiffany was that she was completely oblivious to her powerful sexual allure, it came as naturally to her as breathing. 'I said I'd make tea and toast,' he told her. 'Do you want some?'

When Jeff came down ten minutes later, dressed in pyjamas and an old robe of Mick's, he found them waiting for him with a plate piled high with hot buttered toast and a welcome mug of steaming tea. He took it gratefully and bit into a slice of toast.

'Do you know where she's gone, Tiff?' he asked with his mouth full.

'What makes you think I'd tell you if I did?' she snapped tartly.

Jeff sighed. 'Look, Tiffany, I know you think I've been a bastard, and you've got every right. But Pamela is my wife and, no matter what you might think, I do love her. Christ, can't you see what it's doing to me, not knowing where she is?'

Tiffany glanced uncertainly at Mick who nodded slightly at her.

'All right,' she conceded grudgingly, 'I do know where she is. But I'm not going to tell you,' she said quickly as Jeff's face lit up. 'I'll ring Pamela myself and see if she wants to speak to you.'

150

'Okay. But she has phoned me before – we are still speaking, you know.'

'Nevertheless, that's all I'm prepared to do. Agreed?'

Jeff nodded and watched as Tiffany turned her back on him and punched out numbers on the telephone. She spoke quietly into the receiver when it was answered at the other end, then waited. After a few moments, she put the phone down and turned back to face him. There was a curious expression on her face which he could not interpret.

'She's not in her room,' she told him.

'What do you mean, she's not in her room? It's nearly midnight, for Christ's sake, where else would she be at this hour?'

Tiffany shrugged, her eyes sliding towards Mick and back again. Mick looked uncomfortable.

'Give me the number, Tiffany – I want to find out where she is.'

'I think you'd better go to bed,' Mick interjected firmly. 'You can ring again in the morning.'

'Look—'

'Ring in the morning,' Mick insisted.

Jeff sank back in his seat, all the aggression flowing out of him. He knew he was beaten, and he also knew that if he was to have any chance of winning Pamela back again, he had better not antagonise his in-laws any further.

'Okay,' he conceded tiredly. 'Do you mind if I use the spare room, Tiffany?'

She smiled at him, the first friendly gesture she

had made towards him all evening.

'You're my brother-in-law, aren't you? What did you think – that we'd pack you off to a hotel?'

Pamela and Casey spent the rest of that day and the following night in Casey's room. They took all their meals there, eating when they were hungry, talking, planning, loving by turns.

When at last she emerged, still sleepy, on the second morning, Pamela went back to her room to find that a huge bunch of flowers had been arranged, presumably by the maid, and put in a vase by her bed. Red roses interspersed with gypsophila and dark green leaves were surrounded by tiny pink rosebuds. Propped up against the vase was a ten-by-twelve-inch glossy black and white photograph of Drew Slattery in his heyday. On it he had scrawled in bold black marker pen:

To Pamela, with my love, Drew.

Pamela buried her face in the velvet petals of one scented stem and smiled. Once upon a time she would have been thrilled to receive a signed photograph from Drew Slattery. Even now, she was touched by the gesture, but having witnessed at first hand his thirst for sexual humiliation, she knew she would never feel quite the same way about him again.

A note by the telephone caught her eye and she picked it up. Apparently her sister had telephoned requesting that she should ring her back. Pamela grinned and, picking up the receiver,

152

flung herself on to the bed. Tiffany must be back from Paris and dying to know how her holiday was progressing. She dialled the number and waited for the connection to be made. There was a great deal she wanted to talk about with Tiffany – like how come she and Mick spent one weekend every year here at Elysium Hall?

'Tiff? It's me – Pamela! How are you?' she asked, rolling on to her back and settling in for a long chat.

'I'm fine – you?'

Pamela laughed. 'Don't give me that innocent tone – you knew full well when you sent me here that this place would be good for me!'

Tiffany's warm laughter floated along the telephone wires. 'So – it's doing you good then?'

'You could say that. Is this how you and Mick keep your marriage fresh?'

'You could say that,' Tiffany mimicked cautiously. 'Though we're not into swinging. We just find that the ambience of the place, coupled with all the wonderful *opportunities* they give you there help to spice things up a bit.'

'I see. Well, obviously, being on my own I've been dabbling solo . . . Tiff?'

'Yes?'

'I think that staying here has rather transformed me. You did say I'd come away as a new woman!'

'Pammie!' Tiffany sounded a little alarmed and Pamela chuckled.

'Don't worry – I'm having fun. For the first time

153

in my life I really feel free to let my hair down. Is that what you meant by the ambience of Elysium Hall getting to you?'

'Oh, Pamela – you will be careful, won't you? Don't get in too deep.'

Pamela smiled to herself at the obvious concern in her sister's voice. It was good to have someone care about her that much.

'Don't fret,' she said seriously. 'I can handle it. I had a message that you called me – was that yesterday or earlier this morning?'

She heard Tiffany make an exasperated sound. 'Of course! I swear to God, Pamela, I've got more holes in my memory than a tea strainer! I rang late last night, but you weren't in your room – where were you?'

'In someone else's,' Pamela replied blithely. 'Why did you ring?'

'I was worried about you!' Tiffany protested.

'Tiffany! I'm a big girl, you know, I can take care of myself. Now – *why did you ring*?'

'Jeff's here.'

'Jeff . . . why?' Pamela sat up in bed, sobering instantly at the mention of her husband.

There was a brief silence on the other end of the telephone.

'He's . . . look, Pamela, I think he's really sorry about what's happened. I've never seen him like this before. I didn't tell him where you were but . . . do you think you could talk to him?'

Pamela smiled. 'Sure, no problem.'

'Are you sure?' Tiffany sounded shocked by

Pamela's nonchalance and Pam guessed that her sister hadn't expected her stay at Elysium Hall to have wrought quite such a transformation.

'Is he there?' she asked.

'Um . . . yes, he's in the garden with Mick. Hang on a minute and I'll call him for you.'

Pamela waited while Tiffany went to fetch Jeff. She was glad to have the opportunity to speak to him so quickly – she could ask him to join her at Elysium Hall before she lost her nerve. If he was as dejected as Tiffany said, hopefully he would be only too pleased to agree.

He sounded agitated when he picked up the telephone.

'Pamela? Where have you been? I've been frantic!'

Deliberately misunderstanding him, Pamela said, 'I'm at a health farm in the deepest West Country. How are you?'

'I'm all right. And you know that's not what I meant,' he grumbled. 'Tiffany rang you at nearly midnight and you weren't in your room. The hotel staff couldn't find you, for Christ's sake! What the hell are you playing at, Pamela?'

Pamela was silent for a moment or two as she considered her response. Somehow she could not imagine telling him: *actually, darling, I've met this gorgeous woman who's been teaching me all there is to know about same-gender sex and it's been wonderful* . . . So instead, she countered, 'I've been considering whether you and I have a future together.'

The proverbial wind going out of his sails was almost audible over the telephone. When he spoke, his voice was small, with no trace of the self-righteous anger he had displayed before.

'And have you come to any conclusions?'

'I don't know,' Pamela replied honestly.

To her surprise, there was a choked sound at the other end, and if she didn't know him better, she would have sworn that Jeff was crying. His next words were totally unexpected.

'I love you, Pammie,' he said.

Something seemed to trip in her chest and she knew that she was right not to completely dismiss what they had had together. She felt very emotional as she responded to Jeff's spontaneous declaration.

'I was thinking – we could do with some time to talk things through, away from home. There are things that we'd have to change—'

'Does that mean you don't want us to split up?' he interrupted eagerly.

'I didn't say that, Jeff,' she replied carefully. 'What I did say was that I feel we ought to talk.'

'All right. Of course – just tell me when and where.'

Jeff's eagerness reassured her. Perhaps it would be all right after all.

'Why don't you join me here tomorrow? I'll check it's okay with reception. You could be here by lunchtime.'

There was a pause on the other end of the telephone and Pamela found she was holding her breath, waiting for Jeff's response.

'I'd like that,' he said finally. 'You're obviously . . . enjoying yourself there?'

'Yes.' Pamela smiled. 'Yes, I am. And so will you – trust me. Bye, Jeff.'

Replacing the receiver gently on its cradle, she lay back on the pillows and smiled.

Later, Pamela decided to take a walk in the grounds of the Hall. It was a glorious day, the kind which always made her want to escape outside, to feel the sun on her face and breathe in the sweet, pungent scent of freshly mown grass.

Earlier, she had made the arrangements for Jeff to join her the following day, letting him know that she hoped to see him by lunchtime, and told Casey that everything was going ahead as planned. Now Casey was entertaining herself with Rob, the waiter, and Pamela had decided to opt out of the keep-fit session in favour of doing absolutely nothing except enjoying her own company.

After her conversation with Jeff, she was drawn to the rose garden. There, amongst the scented flowers, she felt quite close to him and she allowed the good memories to creep into her consciousness. Stooping to breathe in the heavenly scent of a particularly lovely yellow bloom, she remembered how he had planted a similar bush in the back garden of their home to mark the occasion of their first wedding anniversary.

'I'll plant it where you'll be able to see it from the kitchen window so that you'll look out while you're cooking or doing the dishes and be reminded of how much I love you.'

Pamela smiled, recalling how she had chosen to overlook the casual chauvinism of his remark because he had sincerely meant the sentiment. And indeed she had looked from the kitchen window while preparing dinner that afternoon, and watched him plant it.

It had been a magical evening. To celebrate their anniversary, at home because they could not afford to go out to eat, she had cooked steak and sauteed potatoes and prepared a huge green salad. Jeff had set up garden candles around the edge of the neat flower-beds and carried their small dining-table out into the garden. Pamela had set it with a lace cloth which her grandmother had given her years before and laid out their best crockery.

'I hope it'll take,' Jeff had fretted, looking at the rose. 'I don't think you're supposed to plant them when they're flowering.'

'I'm sure it will,' she'd reassured him, refilling his glass with the wine he'd brought on his way home from work. 'If we look after it properly – give it plenty of love . . .'

She had trailed off as she saw the way Jeff was looking at her intently in the twilight.

'That's what we must do for each other, Pammie,' he'd said softly, a quaver in his voice which had turned her legs to water. 'We'll nurture our marriage too, won't we?'

158

In reply, Pamela put down her glass and went to join him on the other side of the table. Sitting on his lap, she'd slipped her hand into the open neck of his shirt and placed her palm against his heartbeat. She remembered thinking that she had never felt such complete happiness as she had at that moment. Jeff had felt it too, she was sure of it.

Now she turned away from the yellow roses, hugging the memory to her as she hurried out of the rose garden. It had been so good between them once – surely there had to be a chance that it could be just as good again?

The memory of that anniversary night had left her feeling restless, undeniably aroused as she recalled the passion with which they had celebrated later. Suddenly she found she was looking forward to Jeff's arrival the next day. Somehow she felt more hopeful now.

Turning away from the path that led through the rose gardens and down to the lake, she headed now towards the woodland which bordered the land owned by the Elysium. To her right she could see nothing but acre after acre of rolling farmland. The more familiar view of the formal gardens was to her left while the hotel was behind her. In front was the woodland path.

It was cool beneath the protective canopy of the trees. Pamela welcomed the colder air against the bare skin of her forearms and she lifted her hair off the nape of her neck with one hand to cool herself down. She felt relaxed in a way she hadn't for a long time. This fact surprised her, for she hadn't realised quite how stressed she had become, even before she'd found out about Jeff and Dena.

As she'd dressed in the short-sleeved cotton blouse she was wearing and a comfortable pair of old denim jeans, she had studied herself in the mirror. Perhaps it was her imagination, but she had undergone a minor transformation in the few days since she had arrived at Elysium Hall. Her skin had taken on a kind of glow, her eyes too. Judging by the comfortable fit of her jeans, she had lost a couple of pounds. Would Jeff notice the difference in her?

Pamela smiled to herself at her own conceit. Whether Jeff noticed or not was irrelevant, she knew. It was how she *felt* that was important, and she was aware that the glow she had noticed came from within. Elysium Hall had reawakened her sleeping senses, made her come alive.

Her step lightened as she walked along the pathway. Gathering pace, she swung her arms and breathed in the sweet woodland scent in the air. She felt light: light of heart and light of spirit. Laughing slightly at herself, she decided to veer off the main footpath, turning instead on to a narrow track which appeared to be about to take her into the denser part of the woods.

After she had been walking for a while, Pamela became aware of music drifting on the breeze. It wasn't a sudden noise, more a gradual impingement on her senses and she strained her ears in order to hear it more clearly. It wasn't her imagination – the sound was growing louder as she walked towards it. Someone was playing the guitar in the middle of the woods.

There was something almost surreal about coming across a guitarist in such a dreamlike setting. Pamela found herself breathing more shallowly, as if afraid to disturb the unseen musician. For she didn't want the music to stop; it had an indefinable, yearning quality to it which made her heart ache.

She sensed she was drawing closer and the small hairs on the nape of her neck began to prickle. Her steps slowed and she trod carefully on the mossy ground, afraid to signal her approach. With a sense of almost mystical anticipation, Pamela rounded a bend in the path which unexpectedly opened out into a clearing.

It was quite small, a patch of mossy grass no more than eight feet across. Around the edge of the grass was a ring of spindly toadstools, forming a perfect circle. Pamela gasped, delighted to have come across a genuine fairy ring.

The sunlight slanted down through the tracery of branches above, dappling the grass with light and creating a halo around the guitarist's golden head. He was sitting cross-legged in the middle of the circle, wearing nothing but a pair of faded denims. He looked up and smiled as Pamela approached, but did not stop playing.

'Luke!' she murmured as she recognised him.

Reluctant to step into the magic circle, Pamela sat down just outside and watched him. His skin glowed in the sunlight, like golden velvet. Pamela had a sudden, overwhelming urge to stroke her fingertips across his shoulders and she sat on her hands to suppress it. She noticed that his bare feet were dirty, smeared with green as if he had walked here without shoes. Enchanted, she watched his strong, nimble fingers as they played over the guitar strings.

Even with her limited knowledge of all things musical, Pamela knew that he was gifted. The sounds he coaxed from his guitar were magical: pure, harmonious notes which echoed around the wood, yet seemed not to disturb it.

He played like that for several minutes while Pamela sat and listened and watched. When he finished, the last soaring notes seemed to travel through the trees, dying away as if they had run away from them.

After a moment, Luke put his guitar aside and smiled.

'Hello, Pamela.'

She smiled self-consciously. 'I didn't mean to disturb you. It was so beautiful . . .'

'Thank you. Won't you come closer?'

Pamela glanced at the ring of toadstools and grimaced ruefully.

'I don't know. My grandmother used to tell me that if I stepped inside a fairy ring without the fairy king's permission, I'd be carried away by the elves and lost to the human world forever.'

Luke laughed and held out his arms.

'*I* am the fairy king – come as my guest inside

162

the enchanted circle,' he said.

'You're making fun of me!'

He regarded her soberly, his head slightly on one side. 'Only a little.'

Pamela smiled. 'Do you often come here to play your guitar?'

He didn't answer her, merely smiled enigmatically.

'You have to take off your shoes – the fairies don't like footprints on their land.'

Luke watched as Pamela unlaced her sandals and slipped them off. The moss felt slippery and soft beneath her bare feet and she wriggled her toes, enjoying the sensuous feeling of the soil between them.

'Come on,' he instructed, 'take a chance. Life amongst the elves might well be more fun than your grandmother realised!'

Laughing, Pamela stood up and stepped across the boundary of the fairy ring. Fancifully, she half expected to feel different in some way once she had crossed the barrier. She *did* feel strange, but she had to acknowledge that it was due to a far more earthly influence. As he watched her, Luke's eyes had darkened to a deep, unfathomable blue and Pamela felt her stomach tighten.

'So, *your majesty*,' she said with a shaky curtsey, 'where shall I sit?'

Luke's voice seemed to have dropped an octave, it was so low and mesmerising, and the tension creeping through Pamela's limbs intensified.

'You have to observe the rituals if you want to commune with the fairies,' he told her, only half in jest.

Pamela raised her eyebrows.

'Really? And what rituals are those?'

'You have to touch the four sacred points of the circle all at the same time.'

'The four sacred points?' Pamela repeated disbelievingly.

Luke grinned, a sudden, impish grin which made her heart somersault in her chest.

'Look around you,' he told her infuriatingly.

Pamela ran her eyes around the circle, aware that she wanted very much to sit with Luke in this enchanted place. All she could see was the ring of toadstools, forming an almost perfect circle.

'I don't see anything,' she admitted.

'Look again, more closely. At the daisies,' he explained patiently.

The clearing was sprinkled with daisies and, at first, Pamela did not understand. Then she realised that there were four distinct clumps of the pretty weed at virtually equidistant points on the ring. The clumps were so widely spaced, she immediately realised that the only way she could reach them all at the same time would be to lie spread-eagled on the ground. Glancing uncertainly at Luke, she saw that he knew this, and was waiting to see if she would take up the challenge.

Smiling to herself, Pamela sat down on the soft ground and positioned her feet so that they were just touching two adjacent crops. Then, slowly, she lowered herself on to her back and reached up and out with her arms, straining until she felt the soft petals between her fingertips.

She felt rather than saw Luke rise. He loomed over her, blocking out the sun as he gazed down at her star-shaped body. Pamela felt the tension spread through her belly like warm treacle.

'Hmm,' he murmured, his fists planted firmly on his hips as he towered over her, 'there's something that's not quite right . . . You have to take off your clothes.'

Pamela smiled.

'Now why didn't I think of that?' she said, though she made no move to do so.

Luke sank on to his haunches beside her and brushed a stray wisp of hair away from her cheek.

'You're forgiven,' he said lightly. 'After all, you've never been in a fairy ring before. The fairy king wouldn't expect a mere mortal to know his secrets.'

His fingers felt cool as they deftly unfastened the buttons to her blouse and peeled the sides apart. Pamela saw that his eyes did not linger on the trembling flesh that he exposed and she found herself wanting more and more with each passing second. She lifted her hips as he eased down her jeans and watched as he folded them and her blouse before laying them carefully outside the ring.

She shivered slightly in her plain white cotton undies, goosebumps rising on her flesh as he dispensed with her bra before gently positioning her arms above her head again. Pamela felt the tender leaves of her sex swelling as the backs of his fingers brushed against her mound and she let out a small, involuntary sound of need as he pulled her panties over her ankles.

Placing her underwear neatly on top of her clothes and sandals, Luke turned back towards her and stroked her ankles. Circling each with his fingers, he slowly eased her legs apart so that her toes once again touched the daisies.

Pamela held her breath as her sex-lips parted and she felt the cool kiss of the air against her most sensitive flesh. She imagined how she must look to Luke, open and exposed, the dark, rose pink of her sex-flesh clearly visible. He straightened and stood, looking at her in silence for so long that she felt she would go crazy with anticipation.

'Perfect,' he said at long last. 'Quite, quite exquisite.'

If it wasn't for the tell-tale catch in his voice, Pamela would have thought he was totally unaffected by the sight of her. Squinting slightly into the sun, she ran her eyes over his semi-naked form, trying to gauge from the tightness of his jeans whether he was as aroused as she.

She felt heavy, at one with the mossy earth as she lay there, spread open like a sacrificial offering in front of him. There was indeed something magical about the fairy circle, she decided, for where else could she have fallen so quickly and completely under this sensual spell?

It was a relief when at last he straddled her hips with his feet and bent down to kiss her. His lips were cool as they moved over hers, holding back, denying her the deeper intimacy she craved. As he gazed intently into her eyes, Pamela mused that there were no bonds restraining her, there was no need for her to remain in such an uncomfortable position. And yet she did not move, she remained with her arms and legs straining towards the four sacred points of the ring.

Moving down her body slightly, Luke sank to his knees, one knee either side of her legs. With his fingertips he traced a path from her jawbone down her neck to the dip at her shoulder. His touch was tantalisingly light, making the tiny hairs on her skin rise in awareness and her nipples pucker and harden.

Moulding one breast with his fingers, he brushed them briefly against each crest, making her gasp aloud.

'Close your eyes,' he whispered and she obeyed, without thought.

Once again it occurred to her that she might just as well be blindfolded, her acceptance of his softly voiced command was so total.

Somehow by denying herself one sense, the others became more acute. She was achingly aware of the feel of his fingers as they moved over her skin: beneath the crease of her breasts, along the upward slope and across to the dip of her underarm. Slowly he ran his fingertips along the underside of her arm to her hand where he traced the outline of every finger before retracing his path and crossing over to the other arm.

It was a ritual so slow, so achingly thorough that Pamela felt she would climax purely from the sensation of his fingers edging ever closer to the exposed centre of her. Her belly quivered as he stroked in a circle around her navel and her thighs made an involuntary movement further apart.

Luke ignored her blatant plea for him to touch her where she most longed to be touched. That part of her was left aching, unfulfilled as he caressed the petal-soft skin of her inner thighs and down to her feet. Pamela had never dreamt that the spaces between her toes could be so sensitive, so erotic.

She could feel the wetness of need trickling down between her buttocks and knew that her sex must be glistening in the sunlight. Could he see the moisture gathering between her thighs? Pamela felt like a taut bow-string as he began to work his way back up her legs towards that wet centre. Unable to help herself, she arched her back, pushing her pelvis upward as if to capture his exploring fingers and coax them inward.

She held her breath as he played with the hair on her mons, smoothing it against her skin then running his fingers through it before smoothing it again.

'Luke . . .?' Pamela whispered, his name sounding more like a plea.

'My fairy queen . . .'

Pamela's eyes flew open in surprise as she felt his tongue touch the stem of her clitoris. He circled it delicately twice, then, to her frustration, he stood up.

She watched through half closed eyes as he unbuckled his belt and pulled it through the loops of his jeans. The sound of his zip being drawn down seemed magnified in the still air. He wasn't wearing any underwear, so as he eased his tight jeans over his slim hips, his cock sprang free.

From underneath it looked enormous, long and slender with a slight upward curve. The foreskin had already drawn back to expose the silky head and Pamela longed to enclose it in her hand. Something kept her inert, though, watching and waiting for him to make the next move.

For a moment she thought he was going to enter her immediately, for he knelt down between her spread thighs and lowered himself so that his body was covering hers. He lay there, taking the bulk of his weight on his elbows and knees yet allowing her to feel the strength of his body. With her arms and legs spread wide and Luke's hard torso imprinting itself on her breasts, Pamela felt curiously helpless, like a sacrificial offering, totally without control.

It wasn't an unpleasant feeling and she savoured it, wondering how she could maintain her position with his cock lying like a predatory animal along the crease of her groin.

Luke rested his cheek against hers and she felt how hot he was. His eyes, when they locked with hers, were over bright, almost feverish and his arousal added to hers, making her feel powerful even while she had chosen to be submissive.

Slowly, he began to move his hips back and forth, brushing the length of his shaft lightly across her clitoris in a steady rhythm which made her gasp aloud.

'Oh,' she whispered, 'oh Luke . . .!'

He kissed her, his tongue pushing past the token resistance of her teeth and sweeping the inside of her mouth. In shocking contrast to the tightly controlled movement of his pelvis against hers, he ravished her with his tongue, grinding his lips hard against hers and drawing the sweetness from her mouth.

Pamela could feel the sensations building in her clitoris, could feel the slippery channels of her sex clutching at the rigid shaft of Luke's penis. Turning her hand over she dug her fingernails into the mossy ground, anchoring herself in the grass as she raced towards the peak.

Her toes burrowed into the mossy soil as the first waves broke and she bent her knees, pushing her pelvis upwards to meet the thrust of his penis as he slipped lower and found the entrance to her body. He entered her at the height of her climax and her body drew him in. As the spasms clenched the inside of her vagina, she pulled her mouth away from his and arched her neck, lifting her body up from the ground like a bow as he thrust into her.

Opening her eyes, she imagined she saw small,

translucent figures dancing around the edge of the fairy ring and she cried out, pressing her pulsing clitoris hard against Luke's cock as it moved in and out of her body.

He came with a strangled cry, pulling out of her and splashing the mossy soil with his seed. His arms came about her and held her tightly as she drew up her knees. She wrapped her arms around him and ran her fingers repeatedly over the short blond hairs at the nape of his neck, soothing him.

It seemed like a long time before they stopped shaking and Luke raised his head to look into her eyes.

'You look like a wood nymph,' he said affectionately, running his palm from her breast to her hip.

'A satisfied wood nymph,' she said, pressing her lips against his damp forehead.

He chuckled and they slowly peeled apart. Luke helped Pamela to her feet and they dressed in companionable silence. Picking up his guitar, Luke took Pamela's hand. They both stared down at the ground where the grass had been flattened by their bodies. The moss was darker where Pamela's juices had seeped into the soil. A few drops of semen glistened in the sun.

'Offerings to the fairy king,' he said, squeezing her hand.

Then, with a small bow, he let go of her hand and jumped backwards over the toadstools. Pamela looked at him in astonishment.

'How do you know that you should always leave a fairy ring backwards?'

He shrugged. 'Maybe my grandmother knew yours?'

Pamela smiled.

'I don't think so. I think that you really do believe in fairies!'

And with that, she gave a little bow of her own and hopped backwards out of the fairy ring.

Chapter Ten

THE NEXT DAY was as glorious as the one before and Pamela found herself humming happily as she showered. In preparation for Jeff's arrival, she had booked herself in for hair and beauty treatments all morning, as much to boost her morale as to impress him.

Casey rose and kissed her on the cheek when she came down for breakfast.

'I know you've got a busy morning ahead of you, honey, so I've ordered your breakfast already.'

'That's nice,' Pamela grinned. 'You've not had second thoughts then?'

Casey looked at her with mock offence.

'Second thoughts? Me? You have to be kidding! I'm looking forward to it – especially as you're part of the deal! Just so long as you're sure you can handle it?' she finished on a more serious note.

'I think I can. And even if I'm wrong, and it upsets me, I wouldn't blame you, Casey,' she reassured her.

The two women smiled at each other in complete accord and Pamela reached across the table to give Casey's hand an affectionate squeeze. Just then the waiter arrived with a fresh fruit salad of strawberries, kiwi fruit and banana topped with creamy fromage frais. Afterwards there were newly baked croissants and real butter. Reaching for the frosted jug of freshly squeezed orange juice, Pamela sighed contentedly.

'No matter what happens tonight, at this moment, I'm in heaven!'

Casey laughed and helped herself to one of Pamela's croissants.

'Baby, so long as Jeff is game, tonight you'll be in *seventh* heaven!'

Pamela smiled when she walked into the massage room and found Luke on duty.

'Has the fairy king had to get a day job?' she teased him.

Luke raised an eyebrow at her and affected a haughty expression.

'There isn't much call for my spells these days,' he replied. 'Too many unbelievers. So I've had to resort to mortal methods of healing. Slip off your robe and hop up on to the couch please.'

Pamela let the towelling robe slide slowly off her shoulders to the floor. Holding his eye, she dared him to react as she walked, naked, to the treatment couch, a glint of mischief in her eye as she saw how difficult he found it to keep that look of cool impersonality on his face.

'Do all your clients have this effect on you?' she asked, glancing at the visibly hardening bulge in the front of his sports shorts. 'Or am I just extra lucky?'

'Face down, Pamela,' he said, his voice dangerously low, 'or I might forget this is a professional visit.'

Pamela complied, and he draped a towel discreetly over her bare buttocks. Smiling to herself, she thought how, a few days ago, she would never have dared to be so provocative. It seemed strange now that when she first met Luke she had thought him arrogant and self-obsessed. The little she had found out about him since she liked immensely and it was very clear to her that he was a man who genuinely liked women, treating them as equals whilst revelling in their complex differences.

She closed her eyes as he placed his palms, slippery with warm oil, on her shoulders.

'Mmm, that's lovely,' she muttered, her voice muffled against the towel spread beneath her.

'You're not supposed to say that,' Luke chided gently, a trace of amusement in his voice. 'Not every masseur offers the extra services I provide!'

Pamela chuckled and allowed her body to relax into the couch, encouraged by his skilful fingers. He seemed to know by instinct exactly where to soothe and exactly where to stimulate. Pamela could feel the tension flowing out of her limbs and she felt as if she were melting into the couch.

Luke's fingers could indeed perform magic, she mused. Remembering how wonderful it had been with him in the woods, she considered rolling over and initiating a more intimate massage. But no – Jeff would be arriving at lunchtime and she wanted to save all her energy for the night ahead. With a small, regretful sigh, she allowed the opportunity to pass and closed her eyes.

After what seemed like only a few minutes, Luke leaned forward and blew gently in her ear, making her jump.

'You're going to have to wake up,' he told her. 'My next appointment is due any time now.'

Pamela sat up, disorientated.

'Did I fall asleep?'

'Yep. I'm not sure whether to be flattered or insulted!'

Slipping off the couch, Pamela went over to him and kissed him on the cheek.

'What was that for?' he asked, surprised.

'To say "thank you" for such a lovely massage – and everything else you've done for me this week.'

He watched her as she picked up her robe from the chair where he had folded it earlier and pushed her arms into the sleeves.

'Amanda tells me that your husband is going to join you later today – was that your idea, or his?'

Pamela looked at him in surprise. 'Well, mine. Why do you ask?'

He smiled at her suddenly, and the smile transformed his features, making his eyes crinkle deliciously at the corners.

'I'm glad – you'll let me know if I can help in any way with whatever it is you've got planned for him?'

Pamela laughed, shaking her head. 'You are amazing, Luke, you know that? What is it they teach you here – mind-reading?'

He raised his eyebrows, an enigmatic expression creeping into his eyes.

'I like to keep the source of my powers secret,' he teased her. 'Truthfully – it wasn't difficult to work out what you needed when you first arrived. Some clients are easy to treat – you were one of them.'

'Oh?' Pamela said, intrigued. 'And what was it that I needed?'

Luke shrugged slightly. 'Reaffirmation. A little TLC. Liberation, a little bit of fun – I haven't offended you, have I?'

Pamela shook her head. 'I feel that maybe I *should* be offended – you make me sound like a car in need of an MOT! But strangely, I'm not. How can I be when you're absolutely right? And you've given me all those things. How can I ever thank you?'

Luke smiled again, and this time it was he who bent to kiss Pamela, once on each cheek.

'Just be happy,' he said simply. 'That's reward enough for me.'

Just then a sound in the outer room indicated

that Luke's next client had arrived for his or her massage. They both heard it, and smiled before Pamela turned away, floating out of the treatment room as if she was walking on air.

By lunchtime she had had her hair expertly trimmed and lightened with subtle highlights. Her skin was glowing peachily after her recent facial and she applied her make-up with a light but newly confident touch.

In her room, she dressed in a pale pink sundress and matching, strappy sandals with high heels before applying a little light, flowery perfume to all the pulse points she could think of. Her slightly unfamiliar reflection gazed uncertainly back at her. Then she grinned. She looked good, more than good – she looked fantastic! Whatever Jeff might think, she was happy with her appearance in a way she had never felt happy before.

Feeling happy and confident, Pamela went down to the conservatory and ordered coffee. From a soft armchair by the window, she could see the entrance to the Hall. Sighing contentedly, she picked up a magazine and settled down to wait.

Jeff drew up at the side of the road and pulled out the handwritten map Mick had given him. He knew he'd taken a wrong turning somewhere, but he couldn't work out where he was now. The main roads through the West Country were superb and the drive from Tiffany and Mick's home in London had been as smooth as he could wish for, but since he had turned off into a side road, he felt as if he'd become lost in a Bermuda triangle.

It would help if he could see over the overgrown hedgerows, he mused as he looked out of the car window. The narrow, winding road felt like a tunnel through a maze, the way it was bordered on either side by hedges as tall as he was.

Retracing his route laboriously on Mick's map, Jeff realised that he'd turned left instead of right some miles back. He had virtually doubled back on himself and was now heading back the way he had come. Cursing under his breath, he executed a hasty three-point turn in the middle of the road and turned back.

He was already late. Imagining the interpretation Pamela would put on his tardiness made him groan. How was he going to explain how much he had wanted to be there on time?

It took him another half an hour to find the partially concealed driveway of Elysium Hall. As he manoeuvred his Cavalier between the white pillars of the gateway, he looked around him curiously. There were neatly manicured lawns rolling away at either side of him and what looked like a formal garden up ahead.

As he approached the main entrance, he spotted a woman lying on her back on the grass in the sunshine and his jaw dropped. She was completely naked. Feeling bemused, he pulled into the small car park and took his case out of the boot. His shoes sounded loud as he ran up the wide, semi-circular stone steps and his feeling of being out of place intensified. This wasn't at all what he had expected.

A tall, pretty girl in a neat red suit came out from behind the reception desk to greet him.

'Welcome to Elysium,' she said. Her voice had a lilting, musical quality to it that had Jeff waiting to hear if she would speak again. She did not disappoint him. 'Could you let me have your name so that I can get a porter to put your case in your room?'

'Um, yes – it's Jeff, Jeff Lewis,' he replied quickly.

The girl smiled and, without bothering to consult her guest book, summoned a porter and told him to take Jeff's luggage to room number seventeen.

'I can easily do that myself,' Jeff protested, feeling uncomfortable.

'Certainly not, Mr Lewis – you're expected in the conservatory. This way please.'

She moved across the lobby towards a corridor which led off to the left, leaving Jeff little choice but to follow her. His eyes focusing on the gentle sway of her hips beneath the short red skirt, he admired the movement of her buttocks as she walked. They were firm and high, undulating slightly as she put one leg before the other.

As they reached the conservatory, she turned

and smiled widely at him, catching him off-guard.

'You'll find Mrs Lewis by the window at the far side,' she told him helpfully.

'Thank you.'

Jeff could not stop himself from watching the receptionist as she walked back along the corridor, knowing as he did so that he wasn't even interested in the girl. He was merely using watching her as a diversionary tactic to put off the moment when he would see Pamela. For the truth was that, much as he had wanted to come, now that he was here, he was terrified.

'Hello, Jeff.'

He turned abruptly as his wife's voice sounded close by. He did a double-take. It was Pamela standing a few feet away from him, he knew, and yet it was not Pamela. There was something different about her, something he couldn't quite put his finger on . . . her hair, that was it; she'd altered her hair. Jeff frowned, knowing that wasn't it at all. The change in her was deeper than that, something quite indefinable.

'Did you have a good journey?'

He was jolted out of his tortuous thoughts by her gentle question.

'I'm sorry I'm late,' he blurted, feeling like a fifth-former on his first date. 'It was quite difficult to find the hotel . . .'

'Are you hungry? Only I've had some sandwiches saved for you.'

Uncomfortable with this new awkwardness which had sprung up between them, Jeff was glad of an excuse to move further into the room, cutting short their initial exchange. It was only as he followed Pamela through the jungle of exotic potted plants that he realised that she hadn't kissed him, as she would normally have, nor had he made any move to physically greet her. It seemed like a bad omen.

There was a tall, dark-skinned girl waiting for them at the table. As Jeff approached, she rose to greet him, a friendly, if assessing, smile curving her lips. Pamela touched him on the shoulder.

'Jeff, I'd like you to meet a friend of mine. Casey – this is Jeff.'

'Hello,' Jeff said stiffly, holding out his hand.

Casey looked at his outstretched hand and, for an instant, Jeff thought that she wasn't going to take it. He found himself holding his breath, aware instinctively that this was a crucial meeting, though he did not understand why. When Casey finally curled her fingers around his, he let out an involuntary sigh of relief.

'I'm very pleased to meet you, Jeff,' she said, her voice slipping over his senses like silk-satin over skin.

There was something about the way she was looking at him, an intimate, caressing glint in her beautiful chocolate-brown eyes, that made him feel weak at the knees. He swallowed, hard, before croaking, 'Likewise.'

As he sat down at the round table, between the two women, Jeff caught the glance that passed between them and felt his mouth grow dry. He could not explain why, but this display of feminine solidarity had unnerved him. It was as if Pamela felt the need for a third party between them, as if she was afraid to be with him on her own. The strange thing was, he had the distinct feeling that *he* was the outsider of the trio.

Pamela smiled as she passed him a plateful of salmon sandwiches. He had been hungry as he arrived, but now he found that the bread felt dry in his mouth and he had difficulty swallowing. He gulped gratefully at the tea Casey poured for him and abandoned the sandwich after a few mouthfuls.

'So,' he said after a few minutes of silence, 'what have you been doing with yourself for the past few days?'

Again there was that disconcerting glance between the two women, this time accompanied by a small, complicit smile.

'Oh, you know,' Pamela replied vaguely, 'this and that. How have you been?'

Jeff glanced pointedly at Casey, hoping that she would take the hint and leave them to talk, but the other girl merely smiled serenely at him and poured herself another cup of tea.

'I – I had hoped we could talk,' he said awkwardly. 'You said you wanted to.'

'Of course. Darling – don't mind Casey. We've become very . . . close these past few days.'

'Yes, but—'

'I can leave if you want me to, honey,' Casey interrupted him, directing her words at Pamela.

183

Pam smiled and shook her head. Her hair swished softly against her cheeks and the new highlights caught the sun, making Jeff want to reach out and touch it.

'Of course not. Don't be so stuffy, Jeff – I want you and Casey to get to know each other while you're here.'

Jeff looked from one to the other of them and again he was struck by a strange presentiment of danger. He wanted nothing more than to go with Pamela to her room where they could talk in private – and hopefully end up in bed together. Realising, however, that he was in no position to make demands, at least not yet, he nodded and sipped his tea.

As he listened to the two women talking together, he had to admit that he rather liked Casey. She had a bold, forthright wit which, coupled with an almost animal sensuality, made her powerfully attractive.

Jeff brought himself up short. God, what was he thinking of? He'd come here to make things right with his wife, not to suss out her friends! He felt disgusted with himself and his sense of unease increased.

'Dinner is at eight,' Pamela informed him. 'Why don't we take a walk in the grounds and maybe have a swim beforehand?'

'All of us?' he asked before he could stop himself.

Casey smiled and unfolded her long, lean length from the table.

'I can take a hint – I'll leave you guys to it for now.'

'No!' Jeff was aghast at his own rudeness. 'I didn't mean—'

'No sweat, baby,' Casey soothed, putting one long-fingered hand on his shoulder. 'I'll join you for dinner.'

To Jeff's astonishment, she bent down and pressed her lips against his. He did not respond, merely sitting with his eyes wide open, like a rabbit caught in the beam of a headlight as the tip of Casey's wet tongue probed the closed line of his lips, all too briefly. Then she straightened.

'Have fun, kids!'

Jeff looked at Pamela, but she seemed to be totally unperturbed by her friend's outrageous behaviour. She even smiled at him as she stood up.

'Come on – let's take that walk while the weather's still fine.'

Pamela glanced sidelong at Jeff as they headed towards the rose garden. He still looked stunned by Casey's kiss and she had to hide a smile. His face had been a picture! Poor Jeff – he had no idea what they had planned for him! Feeling a pang of conscience, she tucked her hand into the crook of his elbow and leaned into him slightly as they walked down the steps.

She felt his surprise, but he did not look at her. The warmth of his body was so familiar to her, so dear.

'Smell the roses!' she exclaimed to hide her feelings.

'Where does this path lead?' he asked her as they strolled through the formally laid rose garden.

'There's a lake through the archway there – quite beautiful. I thought we could walk around it and then pass through the woods on our way back to the Hall. Is that okay with you?'

'Anything you say,' Jeff murmured.

Pamela dipped her head to hide her smile, wondering if he would persist with that attitude later?

The lake looked tranquil, a family of swans silently skimming across. The heat of the day had settled into a slightly muggy haze which made walking fairly pleasant, without it being too hot. As they passed the rowing boat which Dirk had used to take her out to the island, Pamela quickened her pace, averting her eyes as her pulse quickened at the memory. How much had happened since then!

'Are the boats available for the guests to use?' Jeff asked unexpectedly.

'Er . . . probably. We'll walk for now though, shall we?'

After a few minutes, Jeff ventured:

'About Dena—'

'We don't have to talk about her,' Pamela interrupted him abruptly. She wanted to nurture the affection she felt towards him, not be reminded of past hurts. He seemed bewildered.

'But I thought you wanted to talk?'

'About *us*, Jeff, and our future together. Unless you're thinking that Dena might have some role to play in that?' she suggested, her voice dangerously low.

'Of course not!' Jeff sounded genuinely shocked. 'I only meant . . . well, I thought you'd want to talk about it,' he finished lamely.

'No. I realise that you and I had probably fallen into something of a rut. I don't think you should have done what you did, but I realise that these things can happen. The question is: where do you want to go from here?'

They had almost circumvented the lake now and had reached the path which led down, through the woods. Pamela could feel Jeff's tension transmitting itself through the arm that she still held.

'I want things to be right between us, Pammie,' he said after a few minutes. 'I want everything to be as it was before.'

Pamela's heart felt squeezed in her chest.

'They can never be the same, Jeff – but that doesn't mean they can't be better.'

'Better?'

He stopped walking and turned her in his arms.

'I think so,' she whispered, her eyes on the familiar outline of his lips.

As he kissed her, she reached her arms up around his neck and pressed herself against him. She could feel the growing hardness at his groin pressing yearningly against her thigh and she broke away regretfully. Not yet.

'Let's walk through here,' she said.

They walked without speaking through the shady woodland, but this time the silence was a companionable one. Their fingers touched, then interlinked, and Pamela felt more hopeful with every step. She thought of her meeting with Luke near the fairy ring. The entire incident had acquired an almost mystical quality in her mind, an unreal tint which had nothing to do with here and now.

'This is a magical place,' she said suddenly. 'Here at Elysium Hall I've been free to find out so much about myself.' She turned her head towards Jeff and smiled, feeling suddenly happy. 'I'm sure you're going to love it too!'

Jeff looked slightly alarmed, but he returned her smile.

'You said something earlier about a swim?' he said.

Pamela grinned. 'We'll go there now.'

Jeff was taken aback by the decor in the Elysium's swimming pool. Pamela watched him from the corner of her eye as she swam up and down. He was swimming in a leisurely breaststroke rather than his usual competitive crawl and his eyes kept swivelling back to the scenes depicted in the mural. She waited for him to say something about it, but he made no comment.

'We'd better change for dinner,' she told him eventually.

'Right.'

He hauled himself out of the pool and Pamela noticed at once that the sexy scenes had aroused him. Seeing her looking at him, Jeff glanced down at his over-stretched swim trunks and grimaced.

'Sorry,' he said.

Pamela climbed out of the water and brushed the backs of her fingers lightly across the front of his crotch. Desire, white-hot and shocking, ripped through her, taking her breath away. She wanted nothing more at that moment than to slip her hand inside his wet costume and grasp the rapidly hardening shaft. From the look on his face she knew that Jeff would not hesitate to respond, should she do so, by lowering her down on the hard white tiles and taking her there and then at the side of the pool.

Fortunately, he was still unsure of her, still careful to let her set the pace. With a small smile of regret, Pamela turned away. It was too soon, and besides, she was determined to go through with the plan she had devised with Casey which, she hoped, would lay the demons to rest once and for all.

Casey was waiting for them at the dinner table.

'Hi,' she smiled as they joined her, her eyes holding a question.

Pamela nodded almost imperceptibly and the other girl beamed at Jeff. With a wary smile, he picked up the menu and made a great show of selecting his meal. He felt squeaky-clean after his swim and the shower which followed and the hair curling at the nape of his neck was still damp.

Sitting between Pamela and Casey, he was unaccountably reminded of the mural painted on the wall at the side of the pool – particularly of the two women – and he felt his cock stir in his trousers. Shifting slightly in his seat, the notion struck him as being inappropriate, yet all through the meal his inexplicable sense of unease persisted.

It didn't really make sense. Pamela had been very sweet to him, although – understandably, he supposed, in the circumstances – she kept a slight distance between them, a barrier which he hoped they would cross tonight.

He had been relieved to find that his bag had been put in Pamela's room, having half expected that she would have booked him into a single, at least until things had been resolved between them. She obviously intended for them to end up in bed together, which was a positive sign that she still wanted him.

That he still wanted her he had no doubt. Watching her now as she talked to Casey, her face animated and her eyes alight with enthusiasm, Jeff felt a mule's kick of desire of the kind he hadn't felt for a long, long time. Suddenly, all he wanted was for the meal to end so that he could take her upstairs and demonstrate to her, in the most basic way, that he loved her.

Perhaps she felt the intensity of his gaze, for at that moment, Pamela turned her head and caught his eye. He watched the recognition flare in her eyes, gloried on the way they darkened as she stared at him. She *did* return his feelings, he was quite sure of it!

Finally the last of the coffee had been drunk and Casey was yawning into her hand.

'Excuse me!' she said, 'you guys must think I'm awful rude! Fact is, I'm just about ready to hit the sack, so I'll say good night. 'Night, honey,' she said, standing up and bending over the table to kiss Pamela on the cheek. 'Jeff.' This time she did not kiss him, merely patting his hand where it lay on the table. 'I may see you both at breakfast tomorrow – or not, huh?'

Jeff's eyes followed her as she sashayed out of the dining-room on her incredibly high heels.

'She's gorgeous, isn't she?'

His head snapped round at the sound of Pamela's voice.

'She's very . . . unusual,' he conceded cautiously.

As if reading his mind, Pamela chuckled. 'Come on – admit it! You'd like to get her into bed, wouldn't you?'

'Absolutely not!' he protested, shocked at her forthrightness.

'You're telling me that you don't fancy Casey?'

'I didn't say that. But there's a world of difference between finding a woman attractive and wanting to drag her into bed at the first opportunity.'

'Really? I thought that was supposed to be

what most men think about most of the time,' Pamela said lightly.

Jeff looked at her suspiciously. 'Is this some kind of test, Pam? Because if it is, let me tell you that I've learned my lesson. I came here to try to *show* you that I'm sorry – I could tell you a million times and still never convince you.'

Pamela gazed steadily at him and he made himself hold her eye, knowing that if winning back her trust was going to be a long, slow process, he had better start in earnest now. After a few minutes, she smiled, a feminine, seductive smile that set his pulses racing.

'Why don't we go upstairs so that you can really *show* me?' she murmured huskily.

Jeff didn't need a second invitation. He stood and went round to her side of the table so that he could help pull out her seat. As Pamela rose, the soft swell of one breast brushed against his upper arm and he felt himself tingle. There was a powerful sexual chemistry at work tonight and he was almost afraid to upset the balance by rushing things.

It felt alien to him to let Pamela set the pace, but he knew that he must if he was to win her back. She tucked her hand in the crook of his arm as they made for the lift and he could feel the weight of her breast as it pressed against his side. Imagining the feel of that perfect, quivering orb in the palm of his hand made him tremble as he pressed the button to call the lift.

As they ascended, he kissed Pamela lingeringly

on the lips, reacquainting himself with the taste and the contours of her mouth. Her body was soft and pliant against his, her lips parting sweetly to allow his tongue access. They reached their floor frustratingly soon.

Their progress along the carpeted corridor was hampered by the number of times they stopped to kiss and fondle one another. As soon as the bedroom door closed behind them, Pamela began to slide his jacket off his shoulders, loosening his tie and pulling at his buttons.

Taking his cue from her, Jeff pushed the straps of her dress over her slender shoulders and eased the bodice downward. Her naked breasts sprung joyously from the constraint and he gathered them up in his palms, delighted that they were not restrained by a bra.

Dipping his head, he enclosed first one nipple, then the other in his hot mouth, bringing them to hardness as he coaxed the tight-fitting dress down over Pamela's hips. His cock leaped in excitement as he realised that she wasn't wearing panties either. He could hardly believe that his normally demure, practical wife had calmly sat eating in a public place without a stitch of underclothing on!

Now she was removing his shirt, kissing her way down the opening so that his flesh rose up in goosebumps and his breath came in short, shallow gasps.

'Oh Pammie!' he whispered. 'I thought I'd never hold you like this again.'

'Ssh!' She thrust her tongue between his lips so that he opened his mouth, as much in surprise as passion, and she silenced him.

He could feel her fingers peeling his belt through the loops of his trousers and he heard the dull thud as it hit the floor. Then she was slipping the fastener apart and drawing down his zip, easing the pressure on his straining penis.

Without quite being aware of how he'd got there, Jeff found himself sitting on the edge of the bed, leaning back on his elbows as Pamela broke off the kiss and straddled him. She was naked now and he wanted to look at her, to savour the beauty of her, but she would not let him. He groaned slightly as she began to kiss around his face, never quite recapturing his mouth, but always tantalisingly near.

'Pamela . . .'

Her tongue swirled around in the dip where his collarbones met and her small teeth nipped playfully at the flesh covering his pectorals. He could feel his penis begin to throb and he reached down to ease his boxers over his hips. His cock sprang free, swaying like a manic baton, pointing straight up from his loins as Pamela's naked form hovered agonisingly close. He tried bucking his hips so that the velvety tip could brush against the soft skin of her belly, but she anticipated him, moving away slightly, just out of reach.

She was smiling, a languid, knowing smile, and Jeff wondered briefly how she had gained this new, powerfully arousing confidence. All rational thought fled as she lowered her head and, unexpectedly, enclosed his exposed cock-head with her lips.

'Oh Lord!' he gasped, leaning more heavily on his elbows as she drew the entire shaft into the hot, wet cavity of her mouth. 'Oh Pamela . . .!'

He felt as if he was on fire, red-hot spirals of sensation travelling from his cock to his spine, all the way up to his skull. His testicles felt tight and full to the point of discomfort and he closed his eyes, arching back his neck until the tendons stood out.

He had never been sucked like this before, certainly not by Pamela. All his nerve-endings seemed to begin and end in those few rigid inches of pulsating flesh as her mouth slid wetly up and down its length. He cried out loud as she allowed him to slip from her mouth for a moment.

'Don't stop!' he gasped, knowing how close he was to the summit. 'Please don't stop – aah!' .

This time she seemed to swallow him to the back of her throat before easing her mouth slowly back up to the tip. There was a gathering of fluid at the base of his cock, a vibrant, tumultuous rush along the stem before his hips bucked and the first hot jags of semen pumped into her silky mouth.

'Yes – oh yes!' he cried brokenly as he came.

As the last drops emerged, he pulled himself so that he was sitting upright and bent down to tangle his fingers in Pamela's hair. It took a few seconds for his brain to recognise that the texture of the hair was all wrong, that the shape of the head still buried in his groin was unfamiliar.

His eyes flew open even as the awful truth dawned.

'Oh my God!' he cried as his suspicions were confirmed. For the eyes now smiling up at him were not grey, but brown and the woman kneeling between his legs was not his wife. 'Casey!' he breathed. Then his shocked eyes flew round the room to lock with Pamela's on the other side of the room. 'What the hell . . .?'

Chapter Eleven

PAMELA GAZED AT the frozen tableau before her with a kind of horrified fascination. Jeff was looking at her in total disbelief, the sleepy, sated expression he had worn seconds before chased away by incredulity. Casey, naked save for the high heeled sandals she had been wearing earlier, sat back on her heels and turned her head towards Pamela too. There was a smear of semen at the corner of her mouth which glistened in the half light and Pamela found herself staring at it, fascinated by her own reactions.

At first when Casey had stealthily joined her by the bed, she had been too caught up in their game plan to do anything other than switch places as they had arranged. Then, as her friend had worked on Jeff and he had raced to his climax without seeming to be aware that a different woman was sucking him, she had been gripped by a surge of jealousy so strong she had had to force herself not to fly across the room and physically drag Casey away.

All the negative feelings she had experienced when she had seen Jeff with Dena came back to her, and for a few moments she had worried that the other, more shocking feelings were not going to come back. But gradually, her eyes fixed on Casey's talented lips as Jeff's cock slid in and out, she had felt the first flutterings of arousal deep within her.

They looked beautiful together; Casey's soft, dark lips encircling the pale pink shaft of Jeff's cock, her throat muscles contracting wildly as she struggled to swallow the results of her expertise. Pamela's fingers had crept down between her legs to fondle the moisture-slicked folds of her own sex as the last of Jeff's climax ebbed away.

Now she was torn between wanting to go to him – and wanting to go to Casey. She looked so utterly delectable kneeling there like a cat who's got the cream, little streaks of semen drying on her perfect black skin . . .

'Pamela . . . my God – why?'

Her head jerked up as Jeff's shocked voice broke the silence. He looked stunned, completely devastated and her heart flipped over in her chest.

'I wanted to watch you . . .' she murmured, aware that her words were slurring, 'I needed—'

'You set me up! The pair of you – you got me here so that you could get your own back by tricking me into—'

'Into what, Jeff? Into experiencing one of the best orgasms of your life? Because that's what it was, wasn't it? I saw your face as you came!'

The flicker of guilt which passed across his features confirmed Pamela's guess and she smiled.

Glancing from one to the other, Casey rose gracefully to her feet and took charge.

'Jeff, baby, that was delicious! Real hot. Now why don't you lean back there at the top of the bed and get your strength back? I'm ready for some honey . . .'

Taking her cue, Pamela stepped forward into Casey's outstretched arms. Both women watched as Jeff, open-mouthed with astonishment, did as he was told. Satisfied that he wasn't about to leave in a huff, Casey turned her attention to Pamela.

'Get on the bed, baby,' she whispered so that only she could hear. 'Let's show him some action that he'll never forget!'

Pamela needed no second invitation. Her legs were trembling with the strength of her arousal, her skin crying out for the sweet touch of Casey's fingers and lips. Aware of Jeff, yet unmindful of him, she went round to the other side of the bed and carefully knelt on it so that she was facing Casey, with her side presented to him.

Casey knelt opposite her and slowly, as if choreographed, the two women moved closer together until their nipples touched. Just that small contact sent spears of excitement travelling through Pamela's belly and she sighed. The other girl swayed slightly from side to side so that her dark-berry nipples brushed gently to and fro over Pamela's fuller, lighter crests.

Using her palms against Pamela's shoulders to steady them both, Casey pushed her tongue between her lips and licked gently across her eyebrows and, when her eyes fluttered to a close, her eyelids. Pamela felt the thin film of saliva dry on the delicate skin as if sealing her eyes closed and tilted her face so that Casey could reach her mouth.

Taking her time, Casey kissed either side of Pamela's nose and round her chin before capturing her parted lips and drawing them into her mouth. Jeff murmured something incoherent as their mouths fused and the kiss deepened, but neither woman heeded him. For now he was no more than a spectator, allowed to remain only to add to their pleasure.

Pamela gave in to the urge to move her hands over Casey's small breasts, kneading the pliant flesh and gently pinching the sensitive nipples before placing her palms at the small of her back and pressing her close. Her own breasts flattened against Casey's and she felt the tender rasp of her pubic hair against her own as their hips ground together.

Casey's skin was slightly damp to the touch and so soft Pamela continuously ran her fingers up and down, revelling in its texture. Her mouth tasted faintly of Jeff and she could smell the sweet, piquant scent of her arousal as she parted her thighs.

Obligingly, Pamela slipped one hand into the warm, wet furrow of her sex, seeking at once the smooth, hard bead of her clitoris. At the same time, Casey reached behind her and, running her fingers along the crease of her bottom, entered her from behind with the first two.

Pamela cried out, involuntarily thrusting her hips back so that Casey's fingers sank in deeper. She murmured in protest when Casey withdrew, opening her mouth without hesitation as she brought the fingers that had been inside her own body to her lips.

'My God!' Jeff groaned as he watched Pamela lick her own juices from the other girl's long, dark fingers.

The atmosphere in the room was electric and Pamela found it was suddenly difficult to breathe. Aware that all eyes were watching her mouth, she slowly and deliberately drew Casey's fingers into her mouth, sucking them with overt relish.

Casey's breath caught in her throat and she pulled her fingers away so that she could ease Pamela down on to her back. Spreading her legs apart, she opened her with her thumbs so that both she and Jeff could see the glistening pink folds of Pamela's sex. Pamela gasped as Casey began to caress her with her lips and tongue, her sharp teeth nibbling gently at her labia, working their way towards her burgeoning clitoris.

Through misty eyes, Pamela saw Jeff kneel up

on the bed. His cock had stiffened and he was stroking it with one hand as he watched Casey. The expression on his face was one of anguished desire and Pamela knew that he was aroused in spite of himself, that he still hadn't quite got over the shock of what was happening.

Casey was kneeling with her taut, almost boyish buttocks thrust up and back so that she could bury her face between Pamela's legs. As Pam watched, Jeff reached out a tentative hand and caressed Casey's bottom.

'Go on, Jeff,' Pamela urged breathlessly, 'I won't mind . . .'

Casey's lips were worrying at the throbbing button at the apex of Pamela's labia. Pamela arched her back and pushed out the tiny bud so that Casey could gain better purchase, drawing it into her mouth and lathing it rhythmically with her tongue.

'Oh yes . . . Casey . . . harder . . . oh!'

The climax surged through her and she gave a shout of triumph. It was the final spur that Jeff was waiting for. With an anguished groan he plunged his rigid shaft between Casey's inviting sex-lips and into the welcoming channel of her body.

With the aftershocks of her orgasm still rippling through her, Pamela scrambled out from under Casey so that she could watch her husband fuck her friend. Jeff was holding Casey by the hips to keep her still as he pistoned in and out of her. Casey's slender body shook under the onslaught, her belly quivering gently under the pressure from within.

Aware that Casey's clitoris was not receiving any stimulation from that angle, Pamela slipped her hand between her legs and began to rub the distended bud. She could feel Jeff's penis moving inside and, despite her recent climax, she felt her swollen sex-flesh respond.

With her other hand she caressed the stretched opening to Casey's body so that Jeff's cock moved in and out of the circle she made with her fingers as it plunged and withdrew. It was slick with the juices from Casey's body and slid easily across her skin.

He was close to coming. His back was arched, his skin glistening with sweat as he laboured towards his second climax. Pamela stepped up the pressure on Casey's clitoris and the other woman squealed as she tipped over the edge.

The contractions of Casey's most intimate muscles squeezed Jeff's cock, milking it so that it wasn't long before he followed her on an upward rush into ecstasy. He sobbed out his release, tears spilling down his cheeks as he collapsed over Casey's back. As he came, Pamela swallowed his cries with her mouth, kissing him deeply, trying to convey her love for him. All three of them collapsed on the bed in a tangle of limbs, all breathing heavily as they separated, then rolled together again.

Pamela ended up sandwiched between Jeff and Casey, upside down on the bed as they all sought to bring their ragged breathing under control.

They were hot and sticky and exhausted, but no one made any attempt to move.

Pamela replayed the scene over and over in her mind, aware that it was one that would feed her sexual fantasies for some time to come. She was filled by a deep and abiding affection for both Casey and Jeff, and she tried to transmit this to them by means of touch.

Characteristically, it was Casey who recovered first.

'I'm going to go back to my room – leave you two to . . . talk,' she said as she extricated herself from the three-way embrace.

Pamela opened her eyes with difficulty and smiled.

'You don't have to go,' she whispered.

Casey leaned over her and brushed a tender kiss across her temple.

'I know. See you tomorrow.'

Pamela and Jeff both watched her as she slipped off the bed and padded over to where she had dropped her clothes.

'Pammie's right – you should stay,' Jeff said as she dressed.

Casey smiled, but shook her head. 'That's very gallant of you, Jeff, honey, but I think you two need a little privacy now, know what I mean?'

Jeff's arm snaked around Pamela's waist and she felt the skin tingle with awareness where his touched. The door clicked softly closed behind Casey and he nuzzled the soft skin behind Pamela's ear.

'I love you,' he murmured huskily.

Pamela curled her back into his sheltering embrace and smiled.

'I love you too,' she replied sleepily. 'Give me an hour or so and I'll show you how much.'

'An hour?' he groaned, 'but I have something for you.'

'I know,' Pamela laughed, feeling his erection pressing into her back. She rolled over to face him on the bed, her expression suddenly serious. 'You don't mind, now?'

'Mind? Why should I mind making love to my own wife?' he said lightly, deliberately misunderstanding her.

'You know what I mean – no, stop that, be serious for a moment,' she said as his hand crept between her legs.

'All right. For a moment.'

'You felt as if you'd been tricked – set up, didn't you?'

He nodded, his lips seeking the damp cup of her shoulder.

'Hmm. For a moment I thought . . .'

'What? What did you think?'

'Nothing. Mmm, you taste divine!'

'Jeff – it's important – I want us to be honest with one another,' she protested, trying not to notice how his lips were moving towards the peak of her breast.

'All right.' He raised his head to look her straight in the eye. 'For a moment I thought you'd made me come all this way just so that you could

205

humiliate me – pay me back for what I'd put you through.'

Pamela was silent for a few minutes.

'You really thought I could do that?' she asked him, her voice small.

'Yes. No. I didn't know – don't you see, Pammie, we've spent so little time together these past few months? I was beginning to lose sight of who you are.'

'I see. Can you see me now?'

Jeff grinned. 'Uh-huh.'

Pamela lifted her chest so that her breasts were pressing against the hard, hair-roughened wall of his chest.

'And do you like what you see?' she murmured throatily.

He didn't reply, at least not with words, merely swooping down on one tumescent nipple and rolling it on his tongue. Pamela sighed, letting the tendrils of desire spread through her, conscious of the moistening and swelling of her most intimate flesh as Jeff caressed the tops of her thighs, edging even closer to the centre of her.

She sighed as his fingers sank gently into the pulpy flesh, opening her smoothly and easing her inner lips apart. Her mouth opened slightly as he sought and found the tiny bundle of nerve endings at their apex and began to tease it with the pads of his fingers.

Jeff leaned over to kiss her, his tongue probing gently in time with his questing fingers. It was such a loving caress, so tender, that Pamela felt her eyes fill with emotional tears. She came quickly with little gasping cries, muffled by his mouth.

Shifting his body so that his cock-head was resting against the entrance to her body, he waited until she opened her eyes before entering her. He licked away the salty tears which glistened on her lashes, content to simply rest inside her as her body rippled around him.

Pamela felt her lower lip tremble as he began to rock his pelvis slightly and he kissed it with tiny, featherlight kisses until it stilled. Holding her gaze, he deepened the penetration so that she could feel the whole length of him inside her.

He was hardly moving, yet she was acutely aware of every nuance of feeling. Her vaginal walls contracted around him, matching his rhythm as he rocked, not thrusting, yet at one with her. His skin was hot as she put her arms around him and they stuck together, breast to breast, thigh to thigh, joined together as if one body.

She knew the moment that the seed began to gather at the base of his cock, could feel the vibration of it as it travelled along his shaft and spilled into her.

'Pamela . . .' he whispered.

'Yes.'

Their mouths fused as his penis slowly deflated inside her. Pamela felt the dampness on her cheeks and realised that he too was silently weeping.

Chapter Twelve

THEY MADE LOVE once more before the golden fingers of dawn pointed through the hastily drawn curtains. They had fallen asleep still joined and Pamela had woken to find Jeff stiffening inside her.

This time she had welcomed the swift thrust of his loins as he rose up on his elbows above her. It had taken a long time for him to reach a climax, during which time Pamela experienced a long, sweetly rippling release of her own.

Now they lay sated, content to hold each other as the birds began to serenade them in the branches of a tree outside the window. Pamela sensed a new tension in Jeff and steeled herself for whatever it was he wanted to say.

'Pamela?' he said at last.

She stiffened, tendrils of dread curling round her spine. Supposing in the cold light of day he had forgotten the perfect togetherness they had achieved last night?

'Hmm?' she murmured reluctantly.

'We ought to talk.'

Jeff rolled on to his side and levered himself up on to one elbow so that he could see her face. Missing the warmth of his body, Pamela shivered and pulled the covers up around her chin.

'What about?'

'How things have . . . changed, for a start. You coming here . . .' he trailed off as if unsure how to continue.

'Go on,' she prompted.

He shrugged, his eyes sliding away from hers and back again.

'I want us to go back to being faithful to each other. I know that might sound rich coming from me since I was the one to break the vows in the first place, but—'

'Jeff.' Pamela stopped him by placing her hand, palm up, against his mouth. 'We've got to put that behind us now.'

His tongue touched the centre of her palm, its wet caress sending little shivers along her arm.

'I know. What about you? Can you put Elysium Hall behind you?'

Pamela thought of Dirk and Luke and Michael, the waiter, and felt a little pang of regret. There was no doubt in her mind, though, that this was the man she wanted permanently in her bed.

'Yes. Except . . .'

'Except?'

Pamela bit her lip, thinking of the promise she

209

had made to Casey.

'I said I'd meet Casey here next time she's over.'

'Oh.'

Jeff looked more thoughtful than offended and Pamela reached up to stroke his cheek.

'You like Casey, don't you?'

He smiled and captured her hand in his.

'Yes. Do you think ... would she consider coming to stay with us, do you think?'

Pamela's heart gave a little leap.

'She might. Especially if we move out of the city.'

'Move ... you mean move house?'

Pamela could see she'd taken Jeff by surprise.

'Yes. It's one of the things I wanted to talk to you about. I hadn't realised how much I missed the farm and living in the countryside. It wouldn't be too far for you to commute and—'

'Whatever you say, Pammie,' Jeff interrupted her, smiling. 'Why don't you invite Casey at breakfast?'

They both looked up as they heard a soft knock at the door.

'Why don't we ask her now?' Pamela suggested, smiling into his eyes. Jeff nodded and they both sat up in bed.

'Come in, Casey,' they called, in unison.

The door opened and Casey slipped inside. She took in the scene with one glance.

'Good morning, my little lovebirds,' she said, walking slowly towards the bed. The filmy

210

negligée she was wearing slipped elegantly off her narrow shoulders and fell to the ground in a silky pool at her feet.

Both Pamela and Jeff held out their arms to her, and Casey smiled as she joined them.

Already published

BACK IN CHARGE
Mariah Greene

A woman in control. Sexy, successful, sure of herself and of what she wants, Andrea King is an ambitious account handler in a top advertising agency. Life seems sweet, as she heads for promotion and enjoys the attentions of her virile young boyfriend.

But strange things are afoot at the agency. A shake-up is ordered, with the key job of Creative Director in the balance. Andrea has her rivals for the post, but when the chance of winning a major new account presents itself, she will go to any lengths to please her client – and herself . . .

0 7515 1276 1

THE DISCIPLINE OF PEARLS
Susan Swann

A mysterious gift, handed to her by a dark and arrogant stranger. Who was he? How did he know so much about her? How did he know her life was crying out for something different? Something . . . exciting, erotic?

The pearl pendant, and the accompanying card bearing an unknown telephone number, propel Marika into a world of uninhibited sexuality, filled with the promise of a desire she had never thought possible. The Discipline of Pearls . . . an exclusive society that speaks to the very core of her sexual being, bringing with it calls to ecstasies she is powerless to ignore, unwilling to resist . . .

0 7515 1277 X

HOTEL APHRODISIA
Dorothy Starr

The luxury hotel of Bouvier Manor nestles near a spring whose mineral water is reputed to have powerful aphrodisiac qualities. Whether this is true or not, Dani Stratton, the hotel's feisty receptionist, finds concentrating on work rather tricky, particularly when the muscularly attractive Mitch is around.

And even as a mysterious consortium threatens to take over the Manor, staff and guests seem quite unable to control their insatiable thirsts . . .

0 7515 1287 7

AROUSING ANNA
Nina Sheridan

Anna had always assumed she was frigid. At least, that's what her husband Paul had always told her – in between telling her to keep still during their weekly fumblings under the covers and playing the field himself during his many business trips.

But one such trip provides the chance that Anna didn't even know she was yearning for. Agreeing to put up a lecturer who is visiting the university where she works, she expects to be host to a dry, elderly academic, and certainly isn't expecting a dashing young Frenchman who immediately speaks to her innermost desires. And, much to her delight and surprise, the vibrant Dominic proves himself able and willing to apply himself to the task of arousing Anna . . .

0 7515 1222 2

THE WOMEN'S CLUB
Vanessa Davies

Sybarites is a health club with a difference. Its owner, Julia Marquis, has introduced a full range of services to guarantee complete satisfaction. For after their saunas and facials the exclusively female members can enjoy an 'intimate' massage from one of the club's expert masseurs.

And now, with the arrival of Grant Delaney, it seems the privileged clientele of the women's club will be getting even better value for their money. This talented masseur can fulfil any woman's erotic dreams.

Except Julia's . . .

0 7515 1343 1

PLAYING THE GAME
Selina Seymour

Kate has had enough. No longer is she prepared to pander to the whims of lovers who don't love her; no longer will she cater for their desires while neglecting her own.

But in reaching this decision Kate makes a startling discovery: the potency of her sexual urge, now given free rein through her willingness to play men at their own game. And it is an urge that doesn't go unnoticed – whether at her chauvinistic City firm, at the château of a new French client, or in performing the duties of a high-class call girl . . .

0 7515 1189 7

A SLAVE TO HIS KISS
Anastasia Dubois

When her twin sister Cassie goes missing in the South of France, Venetia Fellowes knows she must do everything in her power to find her. But in the dusty village of Valazur, where Cassie was last seen, a strange aura of complicity connects those who knew her, heightened by an atmosphere of unrestrained sexuality.

As her fears for Cassie's safety mount, Venetia turns to the one person who might be able to help: the enigmatic Esteban, a study in sexual mystery whose powerful spell demands the ultimate sacrifice . . .

0 7515 1344 X

SATURNALIA
Zara Devereux

Recently widowed, Heather Logan is concerned about her sex-life. Even when married it was plainly unsatisfactory, and now the prospects for sexual fulfilment look decidedly thin.

After consulting a worldly friend, however, Heather takes his advice and checks in to Tostavyn Grange, a private hotel-cum-therapy centre for sexual inhibition. Heather had been warned about their 'unconventional' methods, but after the preliminary session, in which she is brought to a thunderous climax – her first – she is more than willing to complete the course . . .

0 7515 1342 3

DARES
Roxanne Morgan

It began over lunch. Three different women, best friends, decide to spice up their love-lives with a little extra-curricular sex. Shannon is first, accepting the dare of seducing a motorcycle despatch rider – while riding pillion through the streets of London.

The others follow, Nadia and Corey, hesitant at first but soon willing to risk all in the pursuit of new experiences and the heady thrill of trying to out-do each other's increasingly outrageous dares . . .

0 7515 1341 5

SHOPPING AROUND
Mariah Greene

For Karen Taylor, special promotions manager in an upmarket Chelsea department store, choice of product is a luxury she enjoys just as much as her customers.

Richard – virile and vain; Alan – mature and cabinet-minister-sexy; and Maxwell, the androgynous boy supermodel who's fronting her latest campaign. Sooner or later, Karen's going to have to decide between these and others. But when you're shopping around, sampling the goods is half the fun . . .

0 7515 1459 4

INSPIRATION
Stephanie Ash

They were both talented painters, but three years of struggling to make a living from art have taken the edge off Clare's relationship with her boyfriend. The temptation to add a few more colours to her palette seems increasingly attractive – and proves irresistible when she meets the enigmatic and charming Steve.

But their affair is complicated when Steve's beautiful wife asks Clare to paint his portrait as a birthday surprise. Clare is more than happy to suffer for her art – indulging in some passionate studies of her model *and* her client – but when a jealous friend gets involved the situation calls for more intimate inspiration . . .

0 7515 1489 6

DARK SECRET
Marina Anderson

Harriet Radcliffe was bored with her life. At twenty-three, her steady job and safe engagement suddenly seemed very dull. If she was to inject a little excitement into her life, she realised, now was the time to do it.

But the excitement that lay in store was beyond even her wildest ambitions. Answering a job advertisement to assist a world-famous actress, Harriet finds herself plunged into an intense, enclosed world of sexual obsession – playing an unwitting part in a very private drama, but discovering in the process more about her own desires than she had ever dreamed possible . . .

0 7515 1490 X

[ ]	Back in Charge	Mariah Greene	£4.99
[ ]	The Discipline of Pearls	Susan Swann	£4.99
[ ]	Hotel Aphrodisia	Dorothy Starr	£4.99
[ ]	Arousing Anna	Nina Sheridan	£4.99
[ ]	Playing the Game	Selina Seymour	£4.99
[ ]	The Women's Club	Vanessa Davies	£4.99
[ ]	A Slave to His Kiss	Anastasia Dubois	£4.99
[ ]	Saturnalia	Zara Devereux	£4.99
[ ]	Shopping Around	Mariah Greene	£4.99
[ ]	Dares	Roxanne Morgan	£4.99
[ ]	Dark Secret	Marina Anderson	£4.99
[ ]	Inspiration	Stephanie Ash	£4.99
[ ]	Rejuvenating Julia	Nina Sheridan	£4.99
[ ]	The Ritual of Pearls	Susan Swann	£4.99
[ ]	Midnight Starr	Dorothy Starr	£4.99
[ ]	The Pleasure Principle	Emma Allan	£4.99
[ ]	Velvet Touch	Zara Devereux	£4.99
[ ]	Acting it Out	Vanessa Davies	£4.99
[ ]	The Gambler	Tallulah Sharpe	£4.99
[ ]	Musical Affairs	Stephanie Ash	£4.99
[ ]	Forbidden Desires	Marina Anderson	£4.99

X Libris offers an eXciting range of quality titles which can be ordered from the following address:

Little, Brown and Company (UK), P.O. Box 11, Falmouth, Cornwall TR10 9EN

Alternatively you may fax your order to the above address.
FAX No. 01326 317444.

Payments can be made as follows: cheque, postal order (payable to Little, Brown and Company) or by credit cards, Visa/Access. Do not send cash or currency. UK customers and B.F.P.O. please allow £1.00 for postage and packing for the first book, plus 50p for the second book, plus 30p for each additional book up to a maximum charge of £3.00 (7 books plus).

Overseas customers including Ireland please allow £2.00 for the first book plus £1.00 for the second book, plus 50p for each additional book.

NAME (Block Letters) _____

_____

ADDRESS _____

_____

_____

☐ I enclose my remittance for _____

☐ I wish to pay by Access/Visa card

Number _____ Card Expiry Date _____